LEGAL OFFICE TRANSCRIPTION

THIRD EDITION

Tina Kamakaris, B.A., O.T.C.
Professor Emeritus
Seneca College of Applied Arts and Technology
Toronto, Ontario.

OWL PUBLISHING *o/b* TIKAM PUBLISHING INC.
Copyright © 2011 Owl Publishing.
63 Cheeseman Drive, Markham, Ontario L3R 3G3.

LEGAL OFFICE TRANSCRIPTION
Third Edition.

Printed and bound in Canada by Transcontinental Inc.

Interior Design and Composition: Greg Devitt Design

Library and Archives Canada Cataloguing in Publication

Kamakaris, Tina
 Legal office transcription / Tina Kamakaris. -- 3rd ed.

ISBN 978-1-896512-53-2

 1. Legal transcription--Canada--Handbooks, manuals, etc.
2. Legal assistants--Canada--Handbooks, manuals, etc. I. Title.

KE355.S4K34 2011   651'.934   C2011-904040-9
KF320.S4K34

ALSO AVAILABLE BY THE SAME AUTHOR

Legal Office Procedures 6th ed., 2011
Legal Office Procedures Workbook 6th ed., 2011
INSTRUCTOR SUPPORT

Contact Owl Publishing for more information.

Table of Contents

ACKNOWLEDGMENTS

With special reverence, the author wishes to thank Mr. Justice John A. Scollin of the Manitoba Court of Queen's Bench and Mr. Justice Thomas G. Zuber of the Ontario Superior Court of Justice for the privilege of their cameo recordings in this project. The author sincerely appreciates the time that their Lordships took from their judicial calendar to graciously allow us, through their recorded presence, an enchanting, rare backstage visit to the grand halls of justice and the tallest minds of our land.

INTRODUCTION

Welcome to the law firm of **Michael, Eliad & Redford**. For the duration of your *Legal Office Transcription* studies, you will be working with Mr. Robert Bret Redford, a partner in our law firm.

This *Legal Office Transcription* is designed for use with the *Legal Office Procedures* textbook and the *Legal Office Procedures Workbook* both by Tina Kamakaris. Although these publications reflect Ontario law, the *Legal Office Transcription* lends itself to use in any provincial and territorial jurisdiction in Canada.

CD-ROM

The CD that is included with this *Legal Office Transcription* book is a data CD which contains data files and audio files. The audio files that are on the CD are the files that you transcribe on your computer. (The CD is not intended to be played in CD stereo systems). The data files provided on this CD consist of letterhead and memorandum templates. You can open and edit the templates. You can save a copy of your edited work onto your computer's hard drive or onto a removable storage device. (The CD-ROM is a read only device, and files cannot be saved onto the supplied CD).

WHAT IS LEGAL OFFICE TRANSCRIPTION

Typically, legal office transcription consists of listening through a headphone to legal information that is recorded in the form of words (as opposed to music) and keying on paper the words recorded. This type of keying is known as transcription, also referred to as dicta transcription, because you **transcribe**, or convert, the recorded (dictated) information from sound to print.

In the law office, lawyers routinely record (dictate) such items as letters, memos, and documents. The legal assistant or law clerk transcribes the recording on paper using a computer that is equipped with transcription software. The legal assistant or law clerk then submits the transcribed work to the lawyer for the lawyer's review. This is how much of the day-to-day work usually gets done in the law office.

There is a variety of transcription software available, including transcription software that may be universally used and downloaded from the web free of charge, e.g. Express Scribe Transcription Playback Software.

LEGAL OFFICE AUDIO FILES

The CD that is included with this *Legal Office Transcription* book contains recorded legal office audio files in the following areas of law:

1. General Practice, Chapters 1 to 6 in the *Legal Office Procedures* textbook.
2. Litigation, Chapters 7 to 18 in the *Legal Office Procedures* textbook.
3. Family Law, Chapters 19 to 23 in the *Legal Office Procedures* textbook.
4. Corporate and Commercial Law, Chapters 24 to 29 in the *Legal Office Procedures* textbook.
5. Real Estate, Chapters 30 to 38 in the *Legal Office Procedures* textbook.
6. Estates, Chapters 39 to 43 in the *Legal Office Procedures* textbook.

The legal office audio files that are on the CD are designed to help you expand your legal vocabulary and develop the transcription skills that lawyers expect you to possess at work. The files advance gradually, giving you a sense of continuity and meaningful learning while capturing the law office in operation. Once you successfully complete the transcription that is on the CD, you will be ready to begin your legal career with confidence in any area of law in the law office.

Recording by judges   The *Legal Office Transcription* is privileged to give you an extraordinary transcription experience — cameo recordings by two of Canada's most notable justices — the Honourable Justice John A. Scollin, of the Manitoba Court of Queen's Bench, and the Honourable Justice Thomas G. Zuber, of the Ontario Superior Court of Justice. See their respective introductions later in this book.

WHAT'S RECORDED AND WHAT'S NOT RECORDED
RECORDED:

- Paragraph breaks (except for the recording by the justices, which contains no paragraph breaks; such breaks are, however, given in this book).

- The phrase **quote...unquote** in the recording means that you should key opening quotation marks at the beginning of a word or passage and closing quotation marks at the end of the word or passage, e.g. "opening and closing"; similarly, the phrase **bracket...bracket** means that you should key an opening bracket at the beginning of a word or passage and a closing bracket at the end of the word or passage, e.g. (passage).

- Dates are often recorded as **January 2, (this year).** This means that you must key the current year. Similarly, if a date is recorded as **January 2, (last year), key the year prior to the current year.** Some dates are also recorded as **January 2, (seven years ago)**. This means you key **the year of seven years back from the current year**.

  This system of dealing with dates makes the dates continually case-current, no matter when you work on the transcription; for example, if custody is sought for a seven-year old child, it is necessary to the facts of the case that the child's age remain constant at seven years; this dating system accomplishes this important necessity; hence, the child's date of birth would be recorded as January 2, (seven years ago).

NOT RECORDED:

- Punctuation. You are expected to apply correct punctuation.

LEGAL TERMINOLOGY
Each area of law begins with legal terminology exercises that are relevant to and preparatory for your transcription in that particular area of law. This will help you expand your legal vocabulary. Definitions of the legal terms may be found in the Glossary in your *Legal Office Procedures* textbook or in a law dictionary.

GRAMMAR BRUSH-UP

Each area of law contains a variety of grammar refresher exercises. Generally, the grammar refresher exercises are based on the writing principles and punctuation rules that are presented in your *Legal Office Procedures* textbook. You will find helpful explanations, rules, and examples in Chapter 4 of your *Legal Office Procedures* textbook.

GETTING STARTED

Materials and equipment   You require the following materials and equipment:

- Your copy of this *Legal Office Transcription* book.

- Your copy of the *Legal Office Procedures* textbook (a separate publication).

- Your set of headphones.

- A computer with a CD drive and transcription software (your college would usually provide the transcription software).

Names, addresses, etc.   At each item of transcription in this book, you will find correct addresses, correct spelling of names, a list of any unusual words or terms, and other helpful notes to help you with the transcription of that item.

Letters and memos   Unless otherwise instructed, use the full block letter style throughout, this being the letter style that is most commonly used in the profession. Unless otherwise instructed, all memos and letters are to be signed by Robert B. Redford.

Places   To maintain clarity and consistency, the recorded items are set in Toronto, Ontario. You may wish to substitute your city, town, province, and postal code throughout.

Submitting your completed transcription   Your completed transcription should be in good form, i.e. in **mailable** (or perfect) form, ready for signature and mailing. Submit your transcription with a title page containing the following information, or as your instructor may direct:

> Your name
>
> Your instructor's name
>
> Date of submission
>
> Item/s transcribed: (e.g. 1.1, 1.2, 1.3, etc.)

Legal TIP

Create a template of the above information and save it for each subsequent use.

1
GENERAL PRACTICE

LEGAL TERMINOLOGY

To help prepare you for a good transcription start, the following legal terms have been selected from the transcription items that are in the General Practice area of law.

Indicate whether the description of each of the following legal terms is true or false by placing a checkmark in the applicable spaces provided. If necessary, refer to the Glossary in your *Legal Office Procedures* textbook or to a law dictionary:

1. **call to the bar** - when a lawyer completes his or her education and is permitted to practise law. True ____ False ____

2. **plaintiff** - the party who begins a litigation action. True ____ False ____

3. **examination for discovery** - an examination similar to a mini trial where a lawyer asks questions of an opposing party. True ____ False ____

4. **undertakings** - promises to do something. True ____ False ____

5. **without prejudice** - contents that may not be used in evidence. True ____ False ____

6. **statutory** - matters relating to statutes or written laws. True ____ False ____

7. **limitation period** - in litigation, a time limit by which a party must begin an action or lose the right to do so. True ____ False ____

8. **respondent** - a party who responds to a legal proceeding. True ____ False ____

9. **testimony** - a performance on a written test. True ____ False ____

10. **charge/mortgage** - a document drawn up when a party borrows money and places personal property, as opposed to real property, as security for the loan. True ____ False ____

11. **Rules of Civil Procedure** - the formal rules that set out the steps and forms to be followed in civil litigation actions. True ____ False ____

12. **joint venture** - a business enterprise where business parties join together for the purpose of completing a single business project. True ____ False ____

13. **encumber** - the placing on real property of a charge/mortgage or other debt. True ____ False ____

14. **requisitions** - usually, requests by a purchaser's lawyer to have a vendor's lawyer fix problems on title of real property. True ____ False ____

15. **vendor** - in real estate, a party who installs vending machines in colleges. True ____ False ____

16. **agreement of purchase and sale** - in real estate, a contract between a buyer and a seller setting out the terms of a purchase and sale transaction. True ____ False ____

17. **judgment** - a judge's decision at the conclusion of a trial. True ____ False ____

18. **Law Society** - a society which governs the legal profession. True ____ False ____

19. **power of attorney** - a document by which one person gives power to another person to act in the first person's behalf after the first person dies. True ____ False ____

20. **damages** - in civil litigation, an amount of money claimed for injury caused by a wrongful act done to the claimant by another person. True ____ False ____

GRAMMAR BRUSH-UP

Most of the following grammar refresher exercises are based on the principles of writing and punctuation rules that are set out in your *Legal Office Procedures* textbook. For help on any of the following grammar refresher exercises, see Chapter 4 in your textbook.

> **Legal TIP**
>
> A singular subject takes a singular verb; a plural subject takes a plural verb.

> **Legal TIP**
>
> When used as subjects, words such as each, either, neither, another, anyone, anybody, anything, someone, somebody, something, one, everyone, everybody, everything, no one, nobody, nothing take singular verbs.

A. SUBJECT-VERB AGREEMENT - REFRESHER

Double underline the correct verb form from the alternatives given in parentheses.

1. Each of them (was, were) writing a different story.

2. Every one of the lawyers (is, are) to give a speech.

3. More than one parcel of land (is, are) for sale.

4. More of the shareholders (is, are) beginning to attend the meetings.

5. It is you, not he, who (is, are) to be elected.

6. Jack is the only one of the men who always (report, reports) on time.*

7. Whatever they decide (is, are) all right with me.

8. She is one of those women who (is, are) always eager to help.*

9. The jury (take, takes) their seats in the courtroom.

10. The jury (was, were) dismissed.

> **Legal TIP**
>
> Compare:
> Jack is the only one...
>
> She is one of many...

B. SUBJECT-VERB AGREEMENT - REFRESHER

Double underline the correct verb form from the alternatives given in parentheses.

> **Legal TIP**
>
> A singular subject takes a singular verb; a plural subject takes a plural verb.

> **Legal TIP**
>
> Singular subjects joined by "or" "nor" "either-or" or "neither-nor" take singular verb.

> **Legal TIP**
>
> When combining subjects with "or" "nor" "either-or" or "neither-nor," the verb always agrees with the subject nearest to the verb, e.g.
>
> Neither the parents nor the police officer knows what happened in the school yard.
>
> Neither the police officer nor the parents know what happened in the school yard.

1. Neither the jury nor the judge (consider, considers) the evidence compelling.

2. Nobody, not even the top executives, (have, has) access to that information.

3. He is one of those men who (dictate, dictates) too rapidly.

4. James is the only one of the men who always (report, reports) on time.

5. Fifty percent of our students (come, comes) from rural areas.

6. Neither the father nor his sons (want, wants) to hold on to the firm.

7. Not only the committee members but the chairman, too, (favour, favours) the move.

8. Poverty and wealth (have, has) their own temptations.

9. Either Jack or his family members (have, has) to approve it.

10. Neither his cats nor his dog (has, have) any water.

C. POSSESSIVES - REFRESHER

This exercise contains selections from the transcription. Place an apostrophe (') in the place/s where one is required. If the wording contains a correctly applied apostrophe, indicate so by writing correct (C) at the end of the wording which contains the correctly applied apostrophe. See Chapter 4 in your *Legal Office Procedures* textbook for the rules on the use of the apostrophe and possessives.

1.   Our one clients trained bear.

2.   Our two clients trained bear.

3.   The bears tricks and its trainers talent are amazing.

4.   The one applicants lawyer.

5.   Toto, our one sons pet chinchilla.

6.   Toto, our two sons pet chinchilla.

7.   It's Toto, our familys pet chinchilla.

8.   From your husbands testimony.

9.   Your childrens school activities.

10. Your childs school activities.

D. PUNCTUATION - VERBS AND COMMAS

Double underline the correct verb form from the alternatives given in parentheses. Insert any missing commas or apostrophes. Place an x over/next to any incorrect commas or apostrophes. Write a C at the end of any sentences that are correctly punctuated. See Chapter 4 in your *Legal Office Procedures* textbook for the rules and examples on the use of the comma.

1. There should always be some reimbursement in any case of negligence.

2. There are of course a number of ways in which we could do this.

3. Of course you will not need to bring pencils, pens, or pads.

4. Mr. Redford will be pleased certainly with the newly decorated offices.

5. The main reason for the delay in my opinion (was, were) a breakdown in communication.

6. As a rule we do not undertake a job of this magnitude.

7. In short letters convey a definite impression of the firm to it's clients.

8. Mr. Redford (was, were) also invited to speak before the bench in Ottawa.

9. In the first place the rooms at the hotel (is, are) too small for the firms meetings.

10. There should always be some reimbursement in any case of negligence.

Double underline the correct verb form from the alternatives given in parentheses. Insert any missing commas or apostrophes. Place an x over/next to any incorrect commas or apostrophes. Write a C at the end of any sentences that are correctly punctuated. See Chapter 4 in your *Legal Office Procedures* textbook for the rules and examples on the use of the comma.

1. No other nominations (was, were) presented and Mr. Redford was declared elected to the Board of Directors.

2. Cold weather (have, has) damaged the apple crop but the full extent of the loss will not be known until later.

3. In accordance with the instructions in your letter of January 21 I (has, have) signed the form you sent, and am returning it.

4. Mr. Redford said that we should be sure to sign the letters seal them and mail them immediately.

5. Gertrudes aspirations (is, are) to go to college then get a job as a law clerk and later get married.

6. My own experience (indicate, indicates) that Michael, Eliad & Redford deserves it's reputation for being extremely efficient completely, reliable and surprisingly, reasonable in fees.

7. They have opened three womens apparel stores during the past year.

8. The light, green colour of the rooms (contribute, contributes) to the pleasant relaxing atmosphere.

9. The new, legal firm has taken office space in the towns main, professional building.

10. This corporation has paid a regular quarterly dividend without fail each year for the past ten years.

F. PUNCTUATION - VERBS AND COMMAS

Double underline the correct verb form from the alternatives given in parentheses. Insert any missing commas or apostrophes. Place an x over/next to any incorrect commas or apostrophes. Write a C at the end of any sentences that are correctly punctuated. See Chapter 4 in your *Legal Office Procedures* textbook for the rules and examples on the use of the comma.

1. Mr. Redford of Michael, Eliad & Redford in Toronto Ontario will hold interviews next week for law clerks as well as legal assistants.

2. Only one person namely Mr. Robert B. Redford (has, have) a key, for that file.

3. I agree with the speaker that the improvement one (make, makes) not the time one (spend, spends) (is, are) what matters.

4. Robert Redford was somewhat uncertain about the best course of action having worked on that file only two days.

5. Computer manufacturer's produce more than 6.4 million computers or 30 percent of their total output for buyers.

6. By the way she looked spoke and acted one could plainly tell that her main goal, to become law clerk of the firm would be easily reached.

7. At the annual meeting last fall Robert Redford (was, were) elected a director to fill the vacancy caused by John Smiths retirement.

8. In fact, we just sent out a news release announcing that Ms. Nancy Jones' of Waterwell, Ontario, will be law clerk as well as office manager for our law firm.

9. Nancys article on Waterwell Ontario (was, were) the most readable though not the best-written piece in the paper.

10. To make a good impression during the interview one (need, needs) confidence, as well as, experience.

Justice Scollin was appointed to the Court of Queen's Bench for Manitoba in 1981 after practising as a barrister for 27 years.

He was born and educated in Scotland and received his Master of Arts and Bachelor of Laws from the University of Edinburgh, where he was Vans Dunlop Scholar in Law (1947-50). He is a member of the Bars of Scotland, Manitoba, Ontario, and Saskatchewan and was appointed Queen's Counsel (Canada) in 1969 and Queen's Counsel (Manitoba) in 1970.

Following practice as defence counsel in Edinburgh and on circuit in Scotland, Justice Scollin was, in the course of his career, Crown Counsel and a Magistrate in East Africa and, in Canada, Senior Crown Prosecutor for the City of Winnipeg and then a partner in the firm of Pitblado & Hoskin. Later, in Ottawa, he was appointed Assistant Deputy Attorney General of Canada and then Chief General Counsel to the Department of Justice. In addition to assisting in policy preparation and presentation of legislation before the House of Commons and Senate, he appeared frequently before the Supreme Court of Canada and other appellate and trial courts and tribunals as counsel in a diverse range of constitutional, criminal, civil, administrative, and taxation cases.

Justice Scollin also taught the Law of Evidence at the Manitoba Law School and has contributed a text on the *Bail Reform Act* and numerous papers on criminal law and the law of evidence.

Justice Scollin is noted across Canada for the colourful phrasing of his judgments, many of which have appeared in numerous legal publications as outstanding examples of wit and wisdom.

TRANSCRIBED VERSION OF ITEM 1.1

Following is the transcribed version of Item 1.1. Unless otherwise instructed,

(a)   out of class, listen through the dictation while following the transcribed version below just to enjoy Justice Scollin's colourful address to the new lawyers who were called to the Bar, and/or

(b)   transcribe this Item 1.1 while simultaneously following the transcribed version of it which follows below. If so, follow the same format as that shown below.

As I told Ms. Kamakaris, I tried for a week or so in 1961 to become friendly with an ancestor of this dictaphone; however, I had such intimidating lack of success that I (have) ever since dictated to a real live secretary who can either throw her books down or her hands up when I mumble or make mistakes. So, please bear with me and you may find that your vocationally specific skills will be enhanced, if you manage to successfully transcribe this, despite my Scots accent and despite my blushing and faltering advances to this wee machine. So here goes.

I am going to give you, as my second example, remarks that I made in June of 1993 to the new members who were called on that day to the Bar of the Province of Manitoba. This is what I said:

New members of the bar, I congratulate you. Ours is the second oldest profession, and whether we are held in slightly higher or slightly lower esteem than the oldest profession, at least we have a longer shelf life. Indeed the more irreverent among you may view me and some of my colleagues here on the bench as creatures from some juristic Jurassic Park. In any event, I welcome you in the only way that a veteran lawyer can--with words.

In other days and other jurisdictions, it has been common at the call to the bar ceremony for the speaker to put the listeners to sleep under a quilt that he has stitched together with quotes and cliches and paternalistic platitudes about how honourable our profession is. If it were less than honourable, there is little point in telling you now.

Those of you who plan a life in court have to learn only the three-letter alphabet of the advocate: ABC. A is for acuity, the acumen to see, analyze, and judge the issues; B is for brevity, and C is for clarity. The three are inseparable triplets, but my emphasis today is on B for brevity.

First, the general rule of twenty: put your pen down at twenty pages, or your posterior down at twenty minutes. A British judge took two days to charge the jury in a criminal trial. Noting the panel's fatigue, Auberon Waugh, a writer who followed this and many other trials, said: "Twenty minutes, in my experience, is the longest most people are prepared to spend concentrating on the words of a single speaker." With more brevity, Mark Twain said: "Few sinners are saved after the first twenty minutes of a sermon."

Second, if the weather permits, dress your prose in shorts or a miniskirt. If a short word fits, use it. Long words are as depressing as long faces; inevitable sometimes, but you should try to use them only as often as you go to funerals.

Third, do the same with sentences. An overloaded sentence risks sinking like an overloaded tanker. So with paragraphs.

Fourth, get your best argument out first, whether you privately think it's Goliath rather than David. And just in case the judge or tribunal didn't follow you the first time, summarize your best argument at the end.

Fifth. A few words on style. Use the active form rather than the passive. Instead of "It has been suggested by counsel for the plaintiff," write or say "Plaintiff's counsel has suggested." Avoid jargon.

****

1.2 LETTER WITH ENCLOSURE - 191 WORDS

Re: Piccolo v. Fiddler

Inside address:	Mr. John Piccolo 12 Victory Road Toronto, Ontario M4V 2D6
Textbook chapters/precedents:	Chapter 5, Precedents 5.1, 5.2, 5.3 Chapter 4
Dictation names and terms:	Castles, undertakings.

Notes:

1.3 LETTER - 152 WORDS

Re: Piccolo v. Fiddler

Inside address:	Mr. Raymond G. Castles Castles & Sands Barristers and Solicitors Suite 900 205 Portage Street Markham, Ontario L3R 3G3
Textbook chapters/precedents:	Chapter 5, Precedents 5.1, 5.2, 5.3 Chapter 4
Dictation names and terms:	mediation, pre-trial conference, inception, funded, notion, insurers, solely, plaintiffs, subscribe.

Notes:

1.4 LETTER WITHOUT PREJUDICE - 157 WORDS

Re: Piccolo v. Fiddler

Inside address:

Mr. Raymond G. Castles
Castles & Sands
Barristers and Solicitors
Suite 900
205 Portage Street
Markham, Ontario L3R 3G3

Special notation/s:

WITHOUT PREJUDICE

Textbook chapters/precedents:

Chapter 5, Precedents 5.1, 5.2, 5.3
Chapter 4

Dictation names and terms:

arbitration, dismissed, benefits, costs, alleged, overpayment, March, offer.

Notes:

1.5 LETTER - 70 WORDS

Re: Piccolo v. Fiddler

Inside address:

Mr. John Piccolo
12 Victory Road
Toronto, Ontario
M4V 2D6

Textbook chapters/precedents:

Chapter 5, Precedents 5.1, 5.2, 5.3
Chapter 4

Dictation names and terms:

release, services rendered, discounted.

Notes:

Re: Interpretation of the Proceedings Against the Crown Act (PACA) and the Public Authorities Protection Act (PAPA)

Memo to:	David W. Eliad
Textbook chapters/ precedents:	Chapter 6, Precedent 6.3 Chapters 4 and 5
Dictation names and terms:	PACA, PAPA, commissioner, dispute, trained bear, section 5(1)(c), attaching, possession or control of property, scope, *Schenck, and others v. The Queen in Right of Ontario (1982) 40 O.R. (2d) 410, plaintiffs, claiming damages, orchards, road salt, pursuance or execution...of, statutory, statutes, construe, scope, statutory duty, commence, cause of action, alternatively, limitation period, hearing, abide.
Notes:	*Case and/or statute citations are usually given to you in their correct form. You are expected, however, to correctly insert the comma at the year in round or square brackets.

Legal TIP

The phrase "dot, dot, dot," means the ellipsis (...).

1.7 LETTER WITH SECOND PAGE HEADING - 391 WORDS

Re: Tantalus v. Tantalus

Inside address:	Mrs. Imojean Tantalus 96 Tivoli Square Toronto, Ontario M4V 2H6
Textbook chapters/precedents:	Chapter 5, Precedent 5.1 Chapters 4 and 6
Dictation names and terms:	paranoia, bizarre, surveillance cameras, wandering, John, poisoning, Toto, chinchilla, woken, carpet, befriended, environmentally, advocacy, "crystal," pendulum, affecting, "magnetic energy."
Notes:	Remember to set off (block indent) all paragraphs starting with **15** to and including **(g)** as these are a long quotation.

1.8 LETTER WITH SECOND PAGE HEADING - 453 WORDS

Re: Tantalus v. Tantalus

Inside address:	Mrs. Imojean Tantalus 96 Tivoli Square Toronto, Ontario M4V 2H6
Textbook chapters/precedents:	Chapter 5, Second and subsequent page headings Precedents 5.1, 5.2, 5.3 Chapter 4
Dictation names and terms:	cross-examination, excluded property, $75,000.00, inheritance, camcorder, matrimonial home, $60,000.00, $15,000.0, psychiatric, bottled remedies, psychologically, cholesterol, angina, knee.
Notes:	For consistency, express all amounts of money in dollars and cents: $75,000.00.

1.9 LETTER - 291 WORDS

Re: Tantalus v. Tantalus

Inside address:	Castles & Sands Barristers and Solicitors Suite 900 205 Portage Street Markham, Ontario L3R 3G3 Attention: Mr. Raymond G. Castles
Textbook chapters/precedents:	Chapter 5, Precedents 5.1, 5.2, 5.3 Chapter 4
Dictation names and terms:	obstinate, post-dated, magnified, ground, matrimonial home, uncontested, custody, charge/mortgage, car loan, offer to settle, provisions, Rules of Civil Procedure.

Notes:

1.10 LETTER WITH ENCLOSURE - 167 WORDS

Re: Tantalus v. Tantalus

Inside address:	Mrs. Imojean Tantalus 96 Tivoli Square Toronto, Ontario M4V 2H6
Textbook chapters/precedents:	Chapter 5, Precedents 5.1, 5.2, 5.3 Chapter 4
Dictation names and terms:	interim account, incurred, $8,200.00, RRSPs, custody.

Notes:

1.11 MEMO - 123 WORDS

Re: Incorporation of Universal Handout Institute

Memo to:	David W. Eliad
Textbook chapters/precedents:	Chapter 6, Precedent 6.2 Chapters 4 and 5
Dictation names and terms:	John Venus, Mexican, OGYGIA, charitable, worldwide, non-share, interim account.

Notes:

1.12 LETTER - 272 WORDS

Re: Incorporation of Universal Handout Institute in Ontario

Inside address:	Mr. John Venus 96 East Sideroad Toronto, Ontario M4V 2J6
Textbook chapters/precedents:	Chapter 5, Precedents 5.1, 5.2, 5.3 Chapter 4
Dictation names and terms:	OGYGIA, lends, hard assets, lease, Personal Property Security Act (PPSA), encumber, PPSA, encumbrancers, priority, purchase/financing agreement, liquid assets, collateral security, transmission, viability in-depth.

Notes:

1.13 LETTER WITH ENCLOSURE AND SECOND PAGE HEADING - 392 WORDS

Re: Rose sale to Thorn, 95 May Street, Toronto

Inside address:

Mrs. Victoria Rose
8 Justice Road
Toronto, Ontario
M2V 4U6

Textbook chapters/precedents:

Chapter 5, Precedents 5.1, 5.2, 5.3
Chapter 4

Dictation names and terms:

purchaser, hydro arrears, requisitions, agreement of purchase and sale, satisfy himself, searches, utility arrears, notwithstanding, liable, merge, vendor, merge, $4,000.00, whereby, nuisance, judgment, action, competently.

Notes:

1.14 LETTER WITH ENCLOSURE - 366 WORDS

Re: Lerin Estate Matters

Inside address:	Mr. Jason Argonaut 96 Golden Fleece Road Sydney, Nova Scotia B1H 6J4
Textbook chapters/precedents:	Chapter 5, Precedents 5.1, 5.2, 5.3 Chapter 4
Dictation names and terms:	Metropolitan Bank, Yonge Street, Toronto, last will and testament, Alexander Lerin, inventory lists, coins, appraisal, of any age, face value, Law Society, Mr. Pickwick, precursor, filing, powers of attorney, surviving spouse, elect, deceased, one-half, no bar.

Notes:

1.15 MEMO OF LAW - 350 WORDS

Re: Distinctions Between Pain and Suffering and Loss of Expectations of Life

Memo to:	David W. Eliad
Textbook chapters/precedents:	Chapter 6, Precedent 6.3 Chapters 4 and 5
Dictation names and terms:	pain and suffering and loss of expectation of life, Gold's, Damages for Personal Injury and Death in Canada, personal representative, personal injury, wrongdoer, cites, loss of expectation of life, Ontario Trustee Act, estate, deceased, The Law of Damages, Graham, pecuniary, nonpecuniary, trilogy, Supreme Court of Canada, heads, quantum, contends, statutes, causes of actions accruing, mental anguish, impending death.

Notes:

2

LITIGATION

LEGAL TERMINOLOGY

LITIGATION

LEGAL TERMINOLOGY EXERCISE 1

Indicate whether the description of each of the following legal terms is true or false by placing a checkmark in the applicable spaces provided. If necessary, refer to the Glossary in your *Legal Office Procedures* textbook or to a law dictionary:

1. **summary offence** - a less serious crime than an indictable offence which usually occurs only in summertime; also, summary conviction offence. True ____ False____

2. **indictable offence** - a more serious crime than a summary offence. True ____ False____

3. **tort** - a wrongful or negligent act causing harm or injury. True ____ False____

4. **registrar** - the head administrative officer of the court; supervisor of all local registrars. True ____ False____

5. **local registrar** - the local administrative officer in a court office. True ____ False____

6. **affidavit** - a document stating facts which a person swears to be true. True ____ False____

7. **service** - the handing of a court document to a person sued or suing. True ____ False____

8. **proof of service** - evidence that a document has been served on a party in a proceeding. True ____ False____

9. **acceptance of service** - a lawyer's personal acknowledgment of receipt of a document on behalf of a client as well as confirmation that the lawyer represents that client in the action. True ____ False____

10. **admission of service** - a lawyer's acknowledgment of receipt of a document on behalf of a person who is not a client. True ____ False____

11. **personal service** - the personal handing of a court document to a person sued or suing. True ____ False____

12. **alternative to personal service** - the giving of a court document to a party by mail or other means. True ____ False____

13. **issue** - in litigation, a point in dispute; also, a court officer's signing of an originating process. True ____ False____

14. **enter** - in litigation, submitting documents such as judgments and orders to the court for microfilming. True ____ False____

15. **file** - submitting a document to the court office. True ____ False____

16. **commissioner** - a person authorized by law to place people under oath when they wish to swear to the truth of statements they have made in an affidavit. True ____ False____

17. **title of proceeding** - the title of a law book containing legal proceedings.
    True ____ False____

18. **jurat** - the place where a jury sits. True ____ False____

19. **deponent** - a person who makes (swears) an affidavit. True ____ False____

20. **litigation guardian** - a person who represents a litigant under disability, e.g. a minor.
    True ____ False____

Indicate whether the description of each of the following legal terms is true or false by placing a checkmark in the applicable spaces provided. If necessary, refer to the Glossary in your *Legal Office Procedures* textbook or to a law dictionary:

1. **trial court** - a court that deals with trials as opposed to appeals. True ____ False____

2. **appeal court** - a court that makes appeals to a trial court. True ____ False____

3. **statement of claim** - an originating process that begins an action. True ____ False____

4. **statement of defence** - a pleading setting out the defendant's case. True ____ False____

5. **originating process** - a document that begins a proceeding, e.g. statement of claim or notice of application. True ____ False____

6. **plaintiff** - the person who begins a lawsuit. True ____ False____

7. **defendant** - the person who defends a title in a boxing match. True ____ False____

8. **examination for discovery** - in litigation, an oral questioning of the opposite party. True ____ False____

9. **official examiner** - a person whom the Crown appoints to hold examinations for discovery and other examinations. True ____ False____

10. **judgment** - a final decision of the court handed down after trial. True ____ False____

11. **bill of costs** - a court document itemizing a lawyer's fees and disbursements for a party who won judgment and costs. True ____ False____

12. **applicant** - a person who begins a proceeding by way of a notice of application. True ____ False____

13. **respondent** - a person defending an application. True ____ False____

14. **moving party** - a person who provides moving services. True ____ False____

15. **liquidated damages** - a claim for monetary compensation for a debt owing, the amount of which can be clearly calculated, as in a loan. True ____ False____

16. **unliquidated damages** - estimated damages that require the court to determine the amount. True ____ False____

17. **close of pleadings** - that stage of the trial when all pleadings should be served and filed. True ____ False____

18. **deliver** - to serve and file a court document with proof of service. True ____ False____

19. **leave** - a court order to vacate the court room. True ____ False____

20. **privileged** - communication that cannot be disclosed in evidence because the law considers it to be confidential, e.g. communication between lawyer and client. True ____ False____

Indicate whether the description of each of the following legal terms is true or false by placing a checkmark in the applicable spaces provided. If necessary, refer to the Glossary in your *Legal Office Procedures* textbook or to a law dictionary:

1. **attendance money** - money paid to a witness for attending to testify at trial.
    True ____ False____

2. **summons to a witness** - a document requiring a person to attend and give testimony in court. True ____ False____

3. **trial record** - an assembly of key court documents for use by the spectators at trial.
    True ____ False____

4. **reasons for judgment** - a judge's reasons for giving a judgment. True ____ False____

5. **trial brief** - an assembly of key documents that a lawyer intends to refer to at trial.
    True ____ False____

6. **brief of authorities** - a list of decided cases that relate to the case at hand that lawyers use at trial, with a copy given to the judge. True ____ False____

7. **tariff** - in civil litigation, a provincial government schedule of fees and disbursements.
    True ____ False____

8. **costs** - a sum of money the court awards in a judgment to the successful party toward payment of legal expenses. True ____ False____

9. **judgment** - a final decision of the court handed down after trial. True ____ False____

10. **counterclaim** - a pleading that makes a claim for a damaged counter. True ____ False____

11. **crossclaim** - a pleading in which one defendant makes a claim against another defendant.
    True ____ False____

12. **documentary evidence** - evidence given by way of documents, e.g. affidavits.
    True ____ False____

13. **cross-examination** - a lawyer's aggressive questioning of a witness for his or her own party.
    True ____ False____

14. **adverse witness** - a witness for the opposite party. True ____ False____

15. **notice of application** - a document that originates a proceeding that is not an action.
    True ____ False____

16. **factum** - a court document setting out the main facts and the statute and case law which support the case at hand. True ____ False____

17. **notice of motion** - a court document requesting a court order to solve a problem during a proceeding. True ____ False____

18. **order** - a court decision usually resulting from a motion. True ____ False____

19. **default judgment** - a judgment arrived at because the court failed to notify the party to file a response. True ____ False____

20. **writ of seizure and sale** - a court document ordering the sheriff to recover money from a judgment debtor on an unpaid judgment. True ____ False____

GRAMMAR BRUSH-UP

Verb tenses tell when some action happened. The time may be present, past, or future. In addition to describing time, however, verb tenses also indicate whether the verb is expressed in the active or passive voice. Here is a basic overview of verb tense and voice.

SIMPLE TENSE

Present: The present tense describes present action, "I do it now."

Past: The past tense describes an action begun and completed in the past, "I did it already."

Future: The future tense describes future action, "I will do it later."

PERFECT TENSE

Present Perfect: Basically, the present perfect tense describes action begun in the past that continues in the present.

Example: I have searched for three days straight.

Past Perfect: Basically, the past perfect tense describes action completed before a previous past action.

Example: I had searched a long time before I talked to him.

Future Perfect: Basically, the future perfect tense describes action completed before a future action.

Example: I will have searched a long time before you arrive next Sunday, or

I will have searched a long time by then.

VOICE

Verbs express the voice of the action, i.e. whether the action is active or passive. If the verb is active, the subject does the action. If the verb is passive, the subject is acted upon. See Chapter 4 in your *Legal Office Procedures* textbook for information and examples on the use of the passive and active voice. The voice of a verb may be as follows:

Active (A)
Passive (P)
Progressive Active (PA)
Progressive Passive (PP) (exists only in present and past -- not in future and perfect tenses)

Here is a basic summary of the correct use of verb and voice:

Present	**Past**	**Future**
I search (A)	I searched (A)	I will search (A)
I am searched (P)	I was searched (P)	I will be searched (P)
I am searching (PA)	I was searching (PA)	I will be searching (PA)
I am being searched (PP)	I was being searched (PP)	n/a

Present Perfect	**Past Perfect**	**Future Perfect**
I have searched (A)	I had searched (A)	I will have searched (A)
I have been searched (P)	I had been searched (P)	I will have been searched (P)
I have been searching (PA)	I had been searching (PA)	I will have been searching (PA)

Legal TIP

Active voice means the subject does the action, e.g. I search. The subject "I" is doing the searching.

Legal TIP

Passive voice means the subject is acted upon, e.g. I am searched. Someone is doing the searching on the subject "I."

REGULAR VERBS

For each of the following sentences, circle the correct form of the verb from the alternatives given in parentheses.

1. We (cancel, cancelled) our subscription a week ago.

2. Mary said that she (is, was) sorry about the misunderstanding.

3. He said that he (checks, checked) the documents yesterday.

4. He says that he (checks, checked) the documents all the time.

5. Mary now (lived, lives) in the country but (works, worked) in the city.

6. I (am, was) calling him all day yesterday.

7. He says that he (called, will call) you tomorrow.

8. He said that he (called, will call) you yesterday.

9. Frank said that he (works, worked) with Miss Gourley some years ago.

10. Frank says that he (will work, worked) with Miss Gourley next year.

B. VERB TENSE - REFRESHER

REGULAR AND IRREGULAR VERBS

For each of the following sentences, supply the correct form of the past tense of the verb that is given in parentheses. Write your answer in the space provided.

> **Legal TIP**
>
> Generally, irregular verbs are verbs that usually do not end in "ed" when they are expressed in the past tense, e.g. choose=chose, sell=sold, feel=felt.

1. John (break) the record again last month. _____

2. She (drink) the water quickly. _____

3. Last month we (begin) to feel the effects of the weather. _____

4. The wind (blow) hard all day long. _____

5. John (fly) all the way to the Maritimes for the meeting. _____

6. Miss Gourly (write), telling us her decision. _____

7. After our talk, Mr. Redford finally (show) me the records. _____

8. They (build) this factory sometime in the late fifties. _____

9. John (throw) out some very interesting comments. _____

10. The instructor (choose) the textbooks for all subjects. _____

11. John (drive) to the office this morning. _____

12. John (forget) the details of his assignment. _____

13. John (speak) very favourably of his employer. _____

14. The students (ride) all the way by bus. _____

15. Their prices (rise) steeply last month after years of stability. _____

For each of the following sentences, circle the more appropriate form of the verb from the alternatives given in parentheses.

1. Mr. Redford (speaks, has spoken) at the Bar four times already.

2. The directors of Camelot (are choosing, have chosen) Halifax for the upcoming conference.

3. While you (are preparing, prepare) the report, I'll go out to lunch.

4. I (am working, have been working) in Winnipeg for ten years.

5. You (overlook, are overlooking) an opportunity to develop a new software program.

6. We (are giving, have given) her two assignments this past week.

7. John (was looking, looked) for a job when I last saw him.

8. She (has been serving, was serving) as chief executive officer for over a year.

9. They (were registering, have been registering) students last Monday.

10. He (was dictating, dictated) the letters when Mr. Eliad walked in.

11. Mr. Redford (decided, was deciding) on immediate action.

12. I (had been giving, was giving) work to her until Mr. Redford stopped me.

13. He (attended, was attending) graduate school when he was hired.

14. My assistant (has been taking, is taking) summer courses up to now.

15. Wenda (had been training, had trained) for the job for two years.

For each of the following sentences, supply the correct form of the applicable past tense of the verb that is given in parentheses. Write your answer in the space provided.

1.   John has (write) to the law firm. _____

2.   It has been several months since I have (ride) on a train. _____

3.   Fortunately, John had (delay) his departure. _____

4.   Purely by accident, my law clerk has (throw) the paper out. _____

5.   Not one of the passengers had (swim) to the shore _____

6.   John has (bear) all the responsibility for some time. _____

7.   By tonight we shall have (choose) the candidate for you. _____

8.   John has often (speak) about your great sense of humour. _____

9.   John has (forbid) the use of this reference. _____

10. Surely John will not have (forget) our appointment for today. _____

11. John has now (give) us his final reply. _____

12. I think that the assistants have all (go) home by now. _____

13. This error has really (shake) our faith in your law firm. _____

14. Work on the new case has finally (begin). _____

15. Einstein has most certainly (make) enormous contributions to science. _____

E. MISPLACED AND DANGLING MODIFIERS - REFRESHER

From the following pairs of sentences, select the one which is correct. See Chapter 4 in your textbook for rules on the use of misplaced/dangling modifiers:

Legal TIP

Put misplaced modifiers as close as possible to the words they modify, e.g.

___ John only wrote part of his exam.
_x_ John wrote only part of his exam.

Legal TIP

With dangling modifiers, either change the ambiguous modifier or make clear the real subject of the sentence, e.g.

___ Turning the corner, the building came into our sight.
_x_ Turning the corner, we saw the building.

1. ___ We read that Jackie had a baby in her last letter.
    ___ In her last letter, we read that Jackie had a baby.

2. ___ While John was talking on the phone, the doorbell rang.
    ___ While talking on the phone, the doorbell rang.

3. ___ Looking out the window, the mountain view was magnificent.
    ___ Looking out the window, we had a magnificent mountain view.

4. ___ As she was running across the floor, the rug slipped and she lost her balance.
    ___ Running across the floor, the rug slipped and she lost her balance.

5. ___ She almost listened to the whole CD.
    ___ She listened to almost the whole CD.

6. ___ The fire alarm nearly sounded ten times today.
    ___ The fire alarm sounded nearly ten times today.

7. ___ John ordered a hot cup of coffee.
    ___ John ordered a cup of hot coffee.

8. ___ Because John was not hungry, he only wanted some coffee and a donut.
    ___ Because John was not hungry, he wanted only some coffee and a donut.

9. ___ Wendy almost ate all the food on her plate.
    ___ Wendy ate almost all the food on her plate.

10. ___While taking out the trash, the dog kept barking.
    ___While John was taking out the trash, the dog kept barking.

This exercise contains selections from the transcription. Place an apostrophe (') in the place/s where one is required. If the wording contains a correctly applied apostrophe, indicate so by writing correct (C) at the end of the wording which contains the correctly applied apostrophe. See Chapter 4 in your *Legal Office Procedures* textbook for the rules on the use of the apostrophe and possessives.

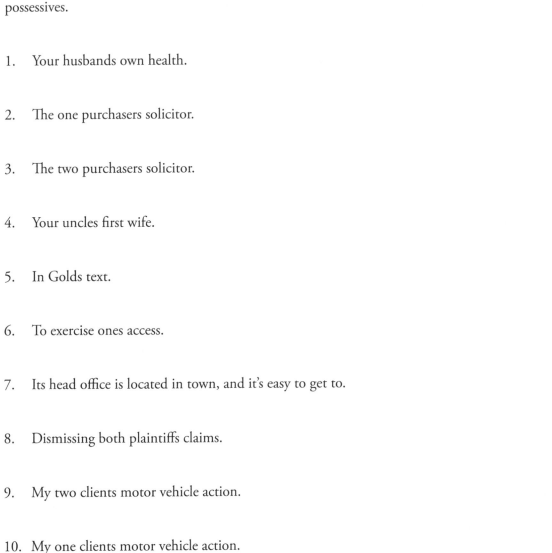

1. Your husbands own health.

2. The one purchasers solicitor.

3. The two purchasers solicitor.

4. Your uncles first wife.

5. In Golds text.

6. To exercise ones access.

7. Its head office is located in town, and it's easy to get to.

8. Dismissing both plaintiffs claims.

9. My two clients motor vehicle action.

10. My one clients motor vehicle action.

This exercise contains selections from the transcription. Place an apostrophe (') in the place/s where one is required. Place an X over/next to any incorrectly applied apostrophes. If the wording contains a correctly applied apostrophe, indicate so by writing correct (C) at the end of the wording which contains the correctly applied apostrophe. See Chapter 4 in your *Legal Office Procedures* textbook for the rules on the use of the apostrophe and possessives.

1.   The Law Societys Errors and Omissions insurer.

2.   The income from the ladies accessories business.

3.   Further to my assistants telephone discussion.

4.   The two defendants solicitors.

5.   The one defendants solicitors.

6.   The husbands mother.

7.   It's head office is located in town, and its' easy to get to.

8.   Your one clients affidavit.

9.   To adjourn todays cross-examination.

10. Examiners office.

Supply the needed punctuation (including commas) in the following sentences. See Chapter 4 in your *Legal Office Procedures* textbook for the rules on the use of the semicolon and colon.

1. Before you make a final decision Mr. Redford let us review these new facts together they shed a good bit of light on the case.

2. That would be a popular choice I am not sure however that it is the best one for you to make under the circumstances.

3. Not all of the profits can be paid out however enough earnings must be retained to permit the investment of capital in research and development expansion and new and better tools.

4. Send the revised list to our offices in St. John's Newfoundland Toronto Ontario Vancouver British Columbia Calgary Alberta Winnipeg Manitoba Moncton New Brunswick Saskatoon Saskatchewan Charlottetown Prince Edward Island and Halifax Nova Scotia.

5. The second report is complete we do not know why the first which we wrote yesterday is not.

6. If these terms meet your approval gentlemen we will ship the following stock items by courier immediately Nos A123 B234 C345 and D456.

7. An important point of course is this you must be prepared when the right opportunity comes your way.

8. The factors we consider first in selecting the person for this position are these aptitude education age and experience.

9. These officers were elected Wendy Forsey president Danielle Michaels vice-president and Vicky Milgard secretary-treasurer.

10. The success of this undertaking hinges largely on one thing your cooperation in carrying out the many and varied tasks that will be required.

Justice Zuber is a supernumerary justice of the Court of Appeal for Ontario and also a regional senior justice of the Ontario Superior Court of Justice in Windsor, Ontario.

Justice Zuber was born in Kitchener, Ontario, and graduated from Assumption College High School in Windsor, Ontario. He received his Bachelor of Arts degree from the University of Western Ontario and his Bachelor of Laws degree from Osgoode Hall Law School. Justice Zuber was called to the bar in 1951. After practising law in the Windsor area for a number of years, he formed the firm of Holden, McMahon, Zuber, Bondy & Cusinato and specialized in counsel work in both civil and criminal law.

Justice Zuber was elected president of the Essex Law Association in 1967, was appointed Queen's Counsel in 1968, and was appointed to the Ontario Court of Appeal in 1975.

From 1955 to 1972, Justice Zuber held a number of academic positions at the University of Windsor. He was a sessional lecturer in commercial and industrial law, a professor of law in the Faculty of Law teaching contracts and civil procedure, and a special lecturer in the Faculty of Law teaching evidence.

In 1986, on the recommendation of the Attorney General, the Lieutenant Governor, with concurrence of the Executive Council, passed an order in council appointing Justice Zuber to the task of inquiring into and reporting on Ontario's court system.

In executing the authority of the order in council, Justice Zuber observed many court operations in Ontario, from the largest in Metropolitan Toronto, to the very smallest in Bruce Mines. He travelled widely throughout the Province of Ontario, from Thunder Bay in the west to Ottawa in the east, and from Windsor in the south to Sudbury in the north. He also visited Quebec and Michigan, U.S.A., and had others visit British Columbia to research their respective court systems.

Justice Zuber released his well known <u>Report of the Ontario Courts Inquiry</u> (Queen's Printer for Ontario, 1987). In it, he made recommendations to the Attorney General concerning "the provision of a simpler, more convenient, more expeditious, and less costly system of courts."

It was Justice Zuber's <u>Report of the Ontario Courts Inquiry</u> that served as the court reform blueprint on which Ontario's new court system was restructured, which new court system came into effect in 1990.

Justice Zuber is also the co-author of <u>Canadian Law</u> (McGraw-Hill Ryerson) and author of <u>Introduction to Canadian Criminal Law</u> (McGraw-Hill Ryerson).

TRANSCRIBED VERSION OF ITEM 2.1

Following is the transcribed version of Item 2.1. Unless otherwise instructed,

(a)   out of class, listen through the dictation while following the transcribed version below to review Justice Zuber's thoughts on reform of the judicial system, and/or

(b)   transcribe this Item 2.1 while simultaneously following the transcribed version of it which follows below. If so, follow the same format as that shown below.

This next excerpt is taken from the last two pages of the <u>Report of the Ontario Courts Inquiry</u> beginning at page 273.

In the foregoing chapters, this inquiry has made a great many recommendations, calculated to rationalize and simplify the justice system in Ontario. The principal objective throughout this report has been to move the justice system closer to the people whom it serves. We have thought it essential that, in those cases which touch all of our lives with increasing frequency, one should be able to exercise one's access to the justice system quickly, economically, and expeditiously. In practical terms, this means that in our matrimonial difficulties, our disputes respecting goods, services and shelter, the transgressions of regulatory laws, and other such cases, we must be able to exercise our right to justice without large expense, waste of time by litigants and witnesses alike, or unnecessary emotional trauma.

In the system proposed by this report, family disputes of any nature or size would go to a single court. That court would have mediation resources available (even before litigation began), and would have simple, expeditious, low cost procedures. Smaller civil cases could be brought before a court with quick, straightforward procedures in a non-adversarial approach like that of the family court.   Criminal cases would proceed faster and without unnecessary appearances in court before trial. All the courts up to the Court of Appeal would be available in all regions of the province.

To some, the justice system is a remote institution whose existence is known only by the cases that catch the attention of the mass media. There will, of course, always be "big cases" in the justice system which, because of their notoriety or importance, are the subject of wide interest and become public spectacles. These spectacular cases, however, tend to distort our perception of the administration of justice, and it is wrong to regard the courts as a distant sensational institution of marginal relevance. The justice system is not a spectator sport involving only a very few, which the rest of us watch with varying degrees of interest and amusement. The justice system is a participatory enterprise in which, directly or indirectly, we all have a very large stake and in which we will all be called eventually to take part as victims, witnesses, party, or juror. We have tried throughout this report to emphasize and facilitate this right to participate by recommending a simpler structure of courts, a more efficient management of them, and a more prudent use of the system.

Having said all of this, however, some reality must intrude. This is not the first inquiry into the justice system. There have been others, and many of them have simply gathered dust. In Chapter 7, this inquiry encouraged those who manage the courts to take the advice of Peters and Waterman's In Search of Excellence and "Do it, fix it, try it." We noted that they should not be paralysed by a fear of failure. This same attitude holds true for the reform of the courts. Nothing will be achieved or improved if nothing is tried. We have attempted to make it clear in this report that the time for action is at hand, the system is in danger, and reform must not wait.

If some of the recommendations in this report do not find favour with the governing authorities, then other recommendations should be devised and implemented promptly. It would be wrong to confuse action with an endless circle of further studies, analyses, and reports which would likely do little more than lead to an eventual paralysis. At this point, we would do well to recall an ancient teaching:

> God is urgent about justice, for upon justice the world depends.
>
> (EXODUS Rabbah Mishpatim 30:19, 24)

****

TEMPLETON, Frederick and Vivian
Re: Negligence

In this file, Frederick and Vivian Templeton have retained us to act for them in an action which concerns the negligence of their former lawyer, Mr. Oscar Dudly. The transcription in this file sequentially carries this file from beginning to end. This type of file continuity adds meaning to your transcription as it enables you to see how a civil litigation file might gradually unfold in the legal office.

WORD Processing

The following information is frequently used in this file. Using the applicable word processing features, create a template and save it for each subsequent use in this file:

Our clients:

Mr. and Mrs. Frederick Templeton
49 Second Avenue
Toronto, Ontario
M8U 2J6

Dear Mr. and Mrs. Templeton:

Re: Templeton v. Dudly

Opposing lawyers:

Mr. Roger Best
Best and Bungle
Barristers and Solicitors
39 Park Avenue
Toronto, Ontario
M6E 1A2

Dear Mr. Best:

Re: Templeton v. Dudly

2.2 LETTER WITH ENCLOSURE - 340 WORDS

Re: Templeton v. Dudly

Inside address:	Mr. Jason Turbot The Law Society of Upper Canada Errors and Omissions Department 20 Queen Street West Toronto, Ontario M5H 3R3
Textbook chapters/precedents:	Chapter 5, Precedents 5.1, 5.2, 5.3 Chapter 4
Dictation names and terms:	Oscar, plaintiffs, undertakings, examinations for discovery, defendants, motion, trial list.

Notes:

2.3 LETTER WITH SECOND PAGE HEADING - 411 WORDS

Re: Templeton v. Dudly

Inside address:	Mr. Roger Best Best and Bungle Barristers and Solicitors 39 Park Avenue Toronto, Ontario M6E 1A2
Textbook chapters/precedents:	Chapter 5, Second and subsequent page headings Chapter 5, Precedents 5.1, 5.2, 5.3 Chapter 4
Dictation names and terms:	Errors and Omissions insurer, Justice Frank, carriage, launch.

Notes:

2.4 LETTER WITH SECOND PAGE HEADING AND ENCLOSURE - 715 WORDS

Re: Templeton v. Dudly

Inside address:

Mr. and Mrs. Frederick Templeton
49 Second Avenue
Toronto, Ontario
M8U 2J6

Textbook chapters/precedents:

Chapter 5, Precedents 5.1, 5.2, 5.3
Chapter 4

Dictation names and terms:

Best, jury, accessories business, examinations for discovery, $80,000.00, $15,000.00, Dr. Crane, Dr. Landers, Worker's Compensation Board, Fred.

Notes:

2.5 LETTER - 140 WORDS

Re: Templeton v. Dudly

Inside address:

Mr. and Mrs. Frederick Templeton
49 Second Avenue
Toronto, Ontario
M8U 2J6

Textbook chapters/precedents:

Chapter 5, Precedents 5.1, 5.2, 5.3
Chapter 4

Dictation names and terms:

Best, statement of claim.

Notes:

Re: Templeton v. Dudly

Inside address:	Dr. Dennis Crane
	Suite 910
	6 Lexington Avenue
	Toronto, Ontario
	M2V 4H6
Textbook chapters/precedents:	Chapter 5, Precedents 5.1, 5.2, 5.3
	Chapter 4
Dictation names and terms:	authorization, diagnosis, prognosis, Mr. and Mrs. Templeton, pain clinic.

Notes:

TO:	Dr. Dennis Crane
	Suite 910, 6 Lexington Avenue
	Toronto, Ontario M2V 4H6
RE:	Frederick Templeton and Vivian Templeton
Textbook chapters/precedents:	Chapter 10, Precedent 10.6
	Chapter 4
Dictation names and terms:	x-ray, sustained.

Notes:

Re: Templeton v. Dudly

Inside address:	Mr. Roger Best
	Best and Bungle
	Barristers and Solicitors
	39 Park Avenue
	Toronto, Ontario
	M6E 1A2

Textbook chapters/precedents:	Chapter 5, Precedents 5.1, 5.2, 5.3
	Chapter 4

Dictation names and terms:	examinations for discovery.

Notes:

Re: Templeton v. Dudly

Inside address:	Mr. and Mrs. Frederick Templeton
	49 Second Avenue
	Toronto, Ontario
	M8U 2J6

Textbook chapters/precedents:	Chapter 5, Precedents 5.1, 5.2, 5.3
	Chapter 4

Dictation names and terms:	jury, Best, undertakings, accessories shop.

Notes:

2.10 LETTER WITH ENCLOSURE - 112 WORDS

Re: Templeton v. Dudly

Inside address:	Mr. Roger Best Best and Bungle Barristers and Solicitors 39 Park Avenue Toronto, Ontario M6E 1A2
Textbook chapters/precedents:	Chapter 5, Precedents 5.1, 5.2, 5.3 Chapter 4
Dictation names and terms:	Red & Gray, 123 Hamilton Street, Toronto, Ontario, M6B 6B6, Rules of Civil Procedure.

Notes:

2.11 LETTER - 55 WORDS

Re: Templeton v. Dudly

Inside address:	Mr. Roger Best Best and Bungle Barristers and Solicitors 39 Park Avenue Toronto, Ontario M6E 1A2
Textbook chapters/precedents:	Chapter 5, Precedents 5.1, 5.2, 5.3 Chapter 4
Dictation names and terms:	defence, medical.

Notes:

2.12 LETTER WITH ENCLOSURE - 135 WORDS

Re: Templeton v. Dudly

Inside address:

Mr. and Mrs. Frederick Templeton
49 Second Avenue
Toronto, Ontario
M8U 2J6

Textbook chapters/precedents:

Chapter 5, Precedents 5.1, 5.2, 5.3
Chapter 4

Dictation names and terms:

Best, Dr. John Kildare, Dr. Crane, x-rays, discovery date.

Notes:

2.13 LETTER WITH SECOND PAGE HEADING AND ENCLOSURE - 1,026 WORDS

Re: Templeton v. Dudly

Inside address:

Mr. and Mrs. Frederick Templeton
49 Second Avenue
Toronto, Ontario
M8U 2J6

Textbook chapters/precedents:

Chapter 5, Precedents 5.1, 5.2, 5.3
Chapter 4

Dictation names and terms:

Tuesday, January 24, Best, admissibility, transcript, Law Society, set aside the order, examination for discovery, setting our case down for trial, trial record, George Johnson, Christopher Martin, reminder, or tickler, system, Worker's Compensation, heroin, photocopier, defence medical, pre-trial.

Notes:

2.14 LETTER WITH ENCLOSURE - 56 WORDS

<u>Re: Templeton v. Dudly</u>

Inside address:	Mr. Roger Best Best and Bungle Barristers and Solicitors 39 Park Avenue Toronto, Ontario M6E 1A2
Textbook chapters/precedents:	Chapter 5, Precedents 5.1, 5.2, 5.3 Chapter 4
Dictation names and terms:	pre-trial conference memorandum, Rules of Civil Procedure.

Notes:

2.15 MEMORANDUM - 327 WORDS

TO:	Robert B. Redford
FROM:	David Eliad
RE:	Templeton v. Dudly
Textbook chapters/precedents:	Chapter 6, Precedent 6.2 Chapters 4 and 5
Dictation names and terms:	Dr. Landers, Dr. Kildare, defence medical, $18,000.00, $20,000.00, $30,000.00, soft, ladies' accessories business, pre-trial.

Notes:

Legal TIP

For consistency, express all amounts of money in dollars and cents: $18,000.00.

2.16 LETTER WITH SECOND PAGE HEADING - 367 WORDS

Re: Templeton v. Dudly

Inside address:
Mr. and Mrs. Frederick Templeton
49 Second Avenue
Toronto, Ontario
M8U 2J6

Textbook chapters/precedents:
Chapter 5, Second and subsequent page headings
Chapter 5, Precedents 5.1, 5.2, 5.3
Chapter 4

Dictation names and terms:
assessment of the damages, Fred, pre-trial, $10,000.00, $15,000.00, general damages, pain and suffering, prejudgment interest.

Notes:

Legal TIP

For consistency, express all amounts of money in dollars and cents: $10,000.00.

2.17 LETTER WITH COPY NOTATION - 130 WORDS

Re: Templeton v. Dudly

Inside address:
Mr. Roger Best
Best and Bungle
Barristers and Solicitors
39 Park Avenue
Toronto, Ontario
M6E 1A2

Textbook chapters/precedents:
Chapter 5, Precedents 5.1, 5.2, 5.3
Chapter 4

Dictation names and terms:
proceeding, prejudgment, undertaken.

Notes:

Legal TIP

For consistency, express all amounts of money in dollars and cents: $60,000.00.

2.18 LETTER - 132 WORDS

Re: Templeton v. Dudly

Inside address:	Mr. Roger Best Best and Bungle Barristers and Solicitors 39 Park Avenue Toronto, Ontario M6E 1A2
Textbook chapters/precedents:	Chapter 5, Precedents 5.1, 5.2, 5.3 Chapter 4
Dictation names and terms:	full and final release, direction, execute, order, dismissing.

Notes:

2.19 LETTER WITH ENCLOSURE - 80 WORDS

Re: Templeton v. Dudly

Inside address:	Mr. and Mrs. Frederick Templeton 49 Second Avenue Toronto, Ontario M8U 2J6
Textbook chapters/precedents:	Chapter 5, Precedents 5.1, 5.2, 5.3 Chapter 4
Dictation names and terms:	settlement, $40,336.25.

Notes:

3
FAMILY LAW

LEGAL TERMINOLOGY

FAMILY LAW

Indicate whether the description of each of the following legal terms is true or false by placing a checkmark in the applicable spaces provided. If necessary, refer to the Glossary in your *Legal Office Procedures* textbook or to a law dictionary:

1.   **domestic contract** - in family law, a contract between parties who are spouses or who are about to become spouses. True _____ False_____

2.   **corollary relief** - in divorce, a relief from severe coronary thrombosis. True _____ False_____

3.   **bigamy** - marrying while being already married. True _____ False_____

4.   **matrimonial home** - in family law, the place where people go to get married. True _____ False_____

5.   **right of possession of matrimonial home** - a right given to the non-owner spouse to live in the matrimonial home, though not to own it. True _____ False_____

6.   **equalization payment** - the net family property of spouses, at dissolution of marriage, divided in half. True _____ False_____

7.   **net family property** - the net value of property that married spouses accumulate during marriage. True _____ False_____

8.   **access** - a non-custodial parent's visitation rights with his or her children. True _____ False_____

9.   **child support** - a non-custodial parent's financial support for his or her children. True _____ False_____

10. **custody** - the legal right of a parent to keep his or her children. True _____ False_____

Indicate whether the description of each of the following legal terms is true or false by placing a checkmark in the applicable spaces provided. If necessary, refer to the Glossary in your *Legal Office Procedures* textbook or to a law dictionary:

1. **joint divorce** - a divorce that is brought by both spouses together. True ____ False____

2. **applicant** - the person who begins a family law case. True ____ False____

3. **separation agreement** - a contract between spouses who are separated.
   True ____ False____

4. **paternity test** - a blood or DNA test proving that a man is or is not the father of a child.
   True ____ False____

5. **marriage licence** - a licence that authorizes persons to get married. True ____ False____

6. **marriage certificate** - a certificate that authorizes persons to get married.
   True ____ False____

7. **divorce** - the formal dissolution of a marriage. True ____ False____

8. **temporary/interim relief** - an order for support or custody until the proceeding is heard.
   True ____ False____

9. **divorce judgment** - a court order that sets out the judge's decision in a divorce case.
   True ____ False____

10. **certificate of divorce** - a court document that certifies the parties to a divorce case are not legally divorced. True ____ False____

GRAMMAR BRUSH-UP

In each of the following sentences, indicate if the sentence is written in the passive or active voice. If a sentence is written in the passive voice, rewrite it in the active voice in the space provided. See Chapter 4 in your *Legal Office Procedures* textbook for help on the passive voice. See also the discussion on verb tense and voice earlier in this *Legal Office Transcription* book.

1. The job was done by him in two weeks' time. Passive____ Active____

   _____

2. We have been helped by you quite a bit. Passive ____ Active ____

   _____

3. Their prices are raised by them every three months. Passive____ Active____

   _____

4. The law firm refers all new employees to the *Legal Office Procedures* manual.
   Passive____ Active____

   _____

5. The award has been received by them for two years in a row. Passive____ Active ____

   _____

From the following sentences, select the one which corrects awkward and misplaced modifiers as well as awkward passive voice. See Chapter 4 in your *Legal Office Procedures* textbook for help on misplaced modifiers and the passive voice. See also the discussion on verb tense and voice earlier in this *Legal Office Transcription* book.

1. ___ We stood watching the parade on the balcony.

   ___ We stood on the balcony, watching the parade.

2. ___ Wenda observed the airplane sitting in an upstairs window.

   ___ Sitting in an upstairs window, Wenda observed the airplane.

3. ___ Mary's report having been prepared, Mr. Redford studied it carefully.

   ___After Mary had prepared her report, Mr. Redford studied it carefully.

4. ___ Since I had studied law, the personnel director was glad to interview me.

   ___ Having studied law, the personnel director was glad to interview me.

5. ___ Being interested in matters of health, my curiosity about innovative treatments is great.

   ___ Being interested in matters of health, I have great curiosity about innovative treatments.

C. POSSESSIVES - REFRESHER

This exercise contains selections from the transcription. Place an apostrophe (') in the place/s where one is required. Place an X over/next to any incorrectly applied apostrophes. If the wording contains a correctly applied apostrophe, indicate so by writing correct (C) at the end of the wording which contains the correctly applied apostrophe. See Chapter 4 in your *Legal Office Procedures* textbook for the rules on the use of the apostrophe and possessives.

1. Their' one daughters school.

2. Your ex-husbands finances.

3. The respondents motion.

4. The retiring partners share of profits.

5. The firms long term liabilities.

6. The partnerships accountant and its banker.

7. Its an all-shareholders meeting.

8. Its a shareholders ledger and its contents.

9. Less than two days notice.

10. The two auditors report.

Re: NIGEL, Wendy Grace
       Separation Agreement

Textbook chapters/precedents: Chapter 19, Precedent 19.3
                                 Chapter 4

Dictation names and terms: Roy William Nigel, Wendy Grace Nigel, matri-
                                 monial home, 601 Stripes Road, Toronto, Ontar-
                                 io, M8L 6U6, Susanna Nigel, Allan Nigel, rights
                                 and obligations, joint custody, access, designation,
                                 Easter, Thanksgiving, mid-afternoon, Christmas
                                 Eve, alternate, make-up access, 100 kilometres, 60
                                 days, vacates, support and maintenance, "Reside"
                                 means, joint title, equalization payment, execute,
                                 transfer/deed, relinquish, charge/mortgage, con-
                                 tract, incur, sole liability, in tort.

Notes: This agreement is a combination of traditional
                                 and modern styles. Backsheet is optional.

Legal TIP

For consistency, express all amounts of money in dollars and cents and in figures only (as opposed to words and figures): $450.00; $250,000.00.

Legal TIP

Small Roman numerals are expressed as follows: (i), (ii), (iii), (iv), (v).

Agreement ending:

   TO EVIDENCE THEIR AGREEMENT, each of the parties has signed this Agreement under seal before a witness.

DATE:

_____   _____
Witness   Roy William Nigel

DATE:

_____   _____
Witness   Wendy Grace Nigel

NESTRUM, Catherine
Re: Divorce

In this file, we obtained a default divorce judgment and a certificate of divorce on behalf of Catherine Nestrum. This basically means that the respondent, i.e. Mrs. Nestrum's husband, did not respond to our application for divorce on behalf of Mrs. Nestrum. Nevertheless, the respondent's lawyers have now served us with a motion to set aside the default divorce judgment. This means that the respondent is challenging the grounds on which we obtained the default judgment and the terms of the divorce judgment.

The transcription in this file sequentially carries this file to completion. This type of file continuity adds meaning to your transcription as it enables you to see how a family law file might gradually unfold in the legal office.

 **WORD Processing**

The following information is frequently used in this file. Using the applicable word processing features, create a template and save it for each subsequent use in this file:

Our client:

Ms. Catherine Nestrum
910 Grove Street
Toronto, Ontario
M8J 1P2

Dear Ms. Nestrum:

Re: Nestrum v. Nestrum

Opposing solicitors:

Mr. Raymond G. Castles
Castles & Sands
Barristers and Solicitors
Suite 900
205 Portage Street
Markham, Ontario
L3R 3G3

Dear Mr. Castles:

3.2 LETTER WITH ENCLOSURE - 176 WORDS

Re: Nestrum v. Nestrum

Inside address:	Ms. Catherine Nestrum 910 Grove Street Toronto, Ontario M8J 1P2
Textbook chapters/precedents:	Chapter 5, Precedents 5.1, 5.2, 5.3 Chapter 4
Dictation names and terms:	default divorce judgment, Madam Justice Lawson, Castles & Sands, motion record, set aside, Legal Aid.

Notes:

3.3 LETTER WITH COPY NOTATION - 172 WORDS

Re: Catherine Nestrum, Certificate No. 47-654321

Inside address:	Legal Aid Ontario Suite 404 375 University Avenue Toronto, Ontario M5G 2G1 Attention: Ms. Wendy Long
Textbook chapters/precedents:	Chapter 5, Precedents 5.1, 5.2, 5.3 Chapter 4
Dictation names and terms:	certificate for legal aid, grounds, cited.

Notes:

3.4 LETTER WITH SECOND PAGE HEADING AND COPY NOTATION - 594 WORDS

Re: Nestrum v. Nestrum

Inside address:	Mr. Raymond G. Castles Castles & Sands Barristers and Solicitors Suite 900 205 Portage Street Markham, Ontario L3R 3G3
Textbook chapters/precedents:	Chapter 5, Precedents 5.1, 5.2, 5.3 Chapter 4
Dictation names and terms:	motion record, set aside, default, Legal Aid, concede, joint custody, struck, Revenue Canada, thrust, trauma, clinical notes, case law, merits, Rule 57.

Notes:

3.5 LETTER - 287 WORDS

Re: Nestrum v. Nestrum

Inside address:	Mr. Raymond G. Castles Castles & Sands Barristers and Solicitors Suite 900 205 Portage Street Markham, Ontario L3R 3G3
Textbook chapters/precedents:	Chapter 5, Precedents 5.1, 5.2, 5.3 Chapter 4
Dictation names and terms:	adjourn, cross-examination, examiner's office, access, unilateral.

Notes:

3.6 LETTER WITH ENCLOSURE - 160 WORDS

Re: Nestrum v. Nestrum

Inside address:	Ms. Catherine Nestrum 910 Grove Street Toronto, Ontario M8J 1P2
Textbook chapters/precedents:	Chapter 5, Precedents 5.1, 5.2, 5.3 Chapter 4
Dictation names and terms:	Madam Justice Jones, obliged, arrears, set aside, garnishment, adjourned, motion.

Notes:

3.7 LETTER WITH ENCLOSURE - 141 WORDS

Re: Nestrum v. Nestrum

Inside address:	Ms. Catherine Nestrum 910 Grove Street Toronto, Ontario M8J 1P2
Textbook chapters/precedents:	Chapter 5, Precedents 5.1, 5.2, 5.3 Chapter 4
Dictation names and terms:	Madam Justice Jones, motion, custody, David, Marilyn, minutes of settlement.

Notes:

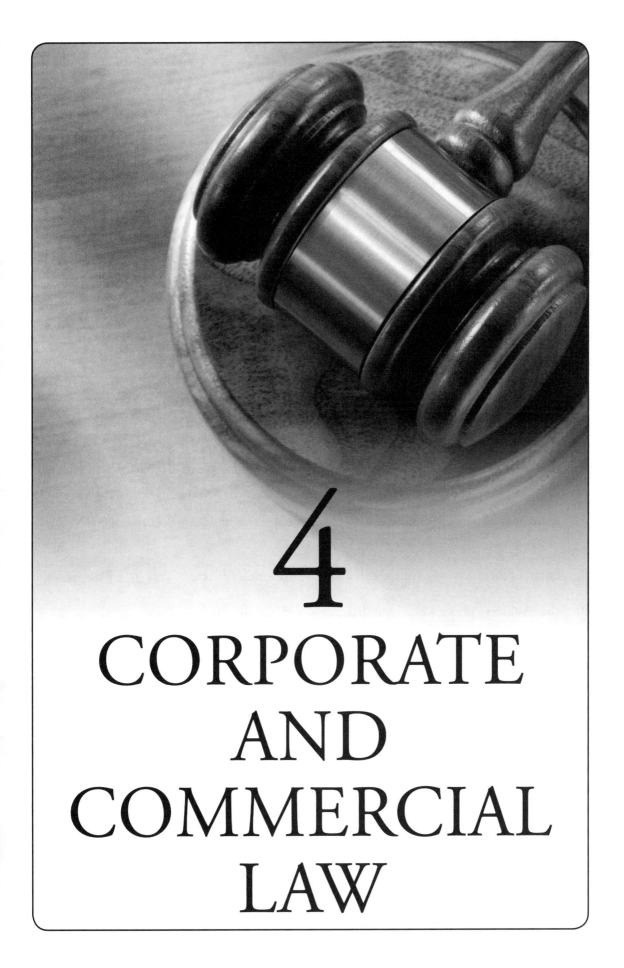

4

CORPORATE AND COMMERCIAL LAW

LEGAL TERMINOLOGY

CORPORATE AND COMMERCIAL LAW

Indicate whether the description of each of the following legal terms is true or false by placing a checkmark in the applicable spaces provided. If necessary, refer to the Glossary in your *Legal Office Procedures* textbook or to a law dictionary:

1.   **sole proprietorship** - an unincorporated business which one person owns.
     True ____ False____

2.   **partnership** - an unincorporated business which two or more people own.
     True ____ False____

3.   **jointly and severally** - rights and obligations shared collectively as well as individually as in partnerships. True ____ False____

4.   **franchise** - a type of business that originated with the French. True ____ False____

5.   **limited liability** - a liability limited to the amount of money a shareholder has paid for a corporation's shares. True ____ False____

6.   **non-offering corporation** - a business corporation that does not sell its shares to the public.
     True ____ False____

7.   **directors** - persons that shareholders elect to manage the affairs of the corporation.
     True ____ False____

8.   **board of directors** - the collective body of a corporation's directors. True ____ False____

9.   **shareholders** - persons who own shares in a corporation. True ____ False____

10. **natural person** - in corporate law, a corporation. True ____ False____

Indicate whether the description of each of the following legal terms is true or false by placing a checkmark in the applicable spaces provided. If necessary, refer to the Glossary in your *Legal Office Procedures* textbook or to a law dictionary:

1. **trade name** - another name by which a corporation transacts business. True ____ False____

2. **common shares** - shares that give voting rights to the holders of them. True ____ False____

3. **preference shares** - shares that usually give voting rights but do not pay dividends to the holders of them. True ____ False____

4. **articles of incorporation** - newspaper articles about a corporation's business services. True ____ False____

5. **certificate of incorporation** - a certificate that certifies that a corporation has been duly incorporated. True ____ False____

6. **by-law** - the permanent laws of a corporation. True ____ False____

7. **resolution** - the formal decisions made by directors and shareholders. True ____ False____

8. **issued shares** - shares that have been sold. True ____ False____

9. **auditors** - Revenue Canada representatives who examine the accounts of all newly incorporated corporations. True ____ False____

10. **initial organization** - the organization of the minute book of a newly incorporated corporation. True ____ False____

11. **resolutions in writing** - formal decisions signed by all of the directors or all of the shareholders of a corporation. True ____ False____

12. **share certificate** - a certificate which certifies that a director's duties may be shared between two directors. True ____ False____

13. **initial notice** - the first notice filed with the ministry after a corporation has been incorporated. True ____ False____

14. **directors' register** - a record of all of the directors of a corporation. True ____ False____

15. **shareholders' register** - a record of all of the shareholders of a corporation. True ____ False____

Indicate whether the description of each of the following legal terms is true or false by placing a checkmark in the applicable spaces provided. If necessary, refer to the Glossary in your *Legal Office Procedures* textbook or to a law dictionary:

1. **shareholder's ledger** - a record of each individual officer. True ___ False___

2. **transfer register** - a record of all share transfers. True ___ False___

3. **quorum** - the minimum number of persons required to be present to conduct a meeting. True ___ False___

4. **proxy** - in corporations, a stand-in representing either the bride or the groom who is absent from the marriage ceremony. True ___ False___

5. **special resolution** - a resolution of the shareholders requiring a two-thirds majority vote to pass. True ___ False___

6. **chattels** - personal property that is movable. True ___ False___

7. **perfection** - registration of a security agreement. True ___ False___

8. **creditor** - a person to whom money is owed. True ___ False___

9. **security agreement** - a contract under which a creditor receives security on personal property as collateral for a loan. True ___ False___

10. **collateral** - something a borrower pledges to a lender as security for a loan. True ___ False___

11. **personal property** - property that is not real estate. True ___ False___

12. **consumer goods** - goods purchased for family or domestic use. True ___ False___

13. **debtor** - a person who owes a debt of money. True ___ False___

14. **security registration** - a registration by a creditor to secure priority of payment from a debtor on a debt involving personal property. True ___ False___

15. **PPSA search** - a check for prior security interests registered on personal property. True ___ False___

GRAMMAR BRUSH-UP

A. SENTENCE FRAGMENTS - REFRESHER

A sentence fragment is a group of words that is only part of a sentence and does not express a complete thought or does not have a subject or a verb. See Chapter 4 in your *Legal Office Procedures* textbook for help on sentence fragments.

Legal TIP

To fix a fragment: If it has no verb, give it a verb; if it has no subject, give it a subject; if it contains a subordinating (transitional) word such as if, when, before, because, although, unless, before, after, since, while, unless, etc., drop the subordinating word.

Indicate which of the following is a fragment (F) and which is a complete sentence (CS).

1. Although John didn't finish the test. F____ CS____

2. John didn't finish the test. F____ CS____

3. The hot weather. F ____ CS ____

4. When preparing legal documents. F ____ CS ____

5. You should pay attention to correct grammar and spelling. F____ CS____

6. And called me umpteen times. F ____ CS ____

7. She called me umpteen times. F ____ CS ____

8. Because it was very late at night. F ____ CS ____

9. I could not finish the paper. F ____ CS ____

10. Driving happily down the scenic road in the country. F ____ CS ____

B. SENTENCE FRAGMENTS - REFRESHER

A sentence fragment is a group of words that is only part of a sentence and does not express a complete thought or does not have a subject or a verb. See Chapter 4 in your *Legal Office Procedures* textbook for help on sentence fragments.

Legal TIP

To fix a fragment: If it has no verb, give it a verb; if it has no subject, give it a subject; if it contains a subordinating (transitional) word such as if, when, before, because, although, unless, before, after, since, while, unless, etc., drop the subordinating word.

1. To run for the provincial party nomination. F ____ CS ____

2. She made a major political decision. F____ CS ____

3. To ask about entering university in the fall. F ____ CS ____

4. He finally decided to see a guidance counsellor. F ____ CS ____

5. My favourite subject is English. F ____ CS ____

6. Although I really like history. F____ CS ____

7. It is my favourite subject. F ____ CS ____

8. I saw "Wuthering Heights." F ____ CS ____

9. Written by Charlotte Bronte. F ____ CS ____

10. Charlotte Bronte wrote it. F ____ CS ____

C. POSSESSIVES - REFRESHER

This exercise contains selections from the transcription. Place an apostrophe (') in the place/s where one is required. Place an X over/next to any incorrectly applied apostrophes. If the wording contains a correctly applied apostrophe, indicate so by writing correct (C) at the end of the wording which contains the correctly applied apostrophe. See Chapter 4 in your *Legal Office Procedures* textbook for the rules on the use of the apostrophe and possessives.

1. The corporations tax returns.

2. The one purchasers counsel.

3. Both corporations gross sales.

4. A corporations gross sales and its profits.

5. The disclosers detriment.

6. An individuals opinion of justice.

7. From both purchasers solicitors.

8. Our two clients address.

9. A solicitors undertaking.

10. From two vendors solicitors.

4.1 LETTER WITH SECOND PAGE HEADING - 339 WORDS

Re: Doctors Jekyll and Hyde - Dental Partnership

Inside address:

Mr. Mark J. Figures
Figures Accounting Associates
Suite 300
400 Digits Road
Toronto, Ontario M4K 2B6

Textbook chapters/precedents:

Chapter 5, Second and subsequent page headings
Chapter 5, Precedents 5.1, 5.2, 5.3
Chapter 4

Dictation names and terms:

restructuring, executing, fax, precedent, beneficiary, management fee, incorporate, compensatory.

Notes:

4.2 PARTNERSHIP AGREEMENT, TRADITIONAL STYLE - 1,345 WORDS

JEKYLL, Craig
HYDE, Allan
Re: Partnership Agreement

Textbook chapters/precedents:

Chapter 24, Precedent 24.1
Chapter 4

Dictation names and terms:

Craig Jekyll, Dalton, Newberry, Allan Hyde, Paton Place, Remington, premises, mutual covenants, sufficiency, incidental, personal property, contemplated, insolvency, discreditation, expulsion, withdrawal, cessation, arbitration, fiscal year, by the then partners, capital, augmented, pro rata, borne, "draw," deficit, practicable, remuneration, belong, partnership money, whatsoever, 20 kilometres, aggregate of, (a) the value, dissolution, sole, absolute discretion, the Income Tax Act, severable, gender, hereunto, seals.

Notes:	Backsheet is optional.

Agreement ending:

IN WITNESS WHEREOF the parties hereto have hereunto set their hands and seals.

SIGNED, SEALED AND DELIVERED
  in the presence of

_____
Craig Jekyll

_____
Allan Hyde

4.3 REPORTING LETTER, INCORPORATION - 1,327 WORDS

Re: Incorporation of Butcher Baker Limited

Inside address:	Mr. John Butcher Butcher Baker Limited Unit 12 345 Republic Road Toronto, Ontario M2W 2H6
Textbook chapters/precedents:	Chapter 5, Second and subsequent page headings Chapter 5, Precedents 5.1, 5.2, 5.3 Chapter 4
Dictation names and terms:	consequences, shareholders' agreement, Business Corporations Act, articles of incorporation, name search, Corporations Information Act (Ontario), negotiable instruments, solvency tests, Securities Act (Ontario), Income Tax Act (Canada), prohibited, natural person, by-laws, status of bankrupt, disqualified, one or more offices, allotment, issuance, Collette Butcher, Dahlia Butcher, John Butcher, Brenda Baker, duly, organizational minutes, shareholders' ledgers, execution, (a) the chair, formality, affixed, the act contemplates, initial notice, notice of change.

(Set-up should look like this)

Shareholder	No. of Shares	Class	Cert. No.	Price per Share
Collette Butcher	1	Common	1	$0.01
Dahlia Butcher	1	Common	2	$0.01

NEW FILE 🗁

BUTCHER BAKER LIMITED

Re: Sale of Shares

We acted for the incorporation of this corporation. The corporation is now interested in selling all of its shares, and numerous steps and documents need to be completed. The transcription in this file sequentially carries this file through numerous steps and documents. This type of file continuity adds meaning to your transcription as it enables you to see how corporation files might gradually unfold in the legal office.

WORD Processing

The following information is frequently used in this file. Using the applicable word processing features, create a template and save it for each subsequent use in this file:

Our client:

Butcher Baker Limited
Unit 12
345 Republic Road
Toronto, Ontario
M2W 2H6

4.4 LETTER WITH SECOND PAGE HEADING - 372 WORDS

Re: Proposed sale of All Shares of Butcher Baker Limited

Inside address:

Mr. John Butcher
Butcher Baker Limited
Unit 12
345 Republic Road
Toronto, Ontario
M2W 2H6

Textbook chapters/precedents:	Chapter 5, Second and subsequent page headings
	Chapter 5, Precedents 5.1, 5.2, 5.3
	Chapter 4

| Dictation names and terms: | retainer, disburse, tabled, non-competition agreement, $7,000.00, $10,000.00, venture, flat, $4,000.00. |

Notes:

4.5 ESCROW AGREEMENT, MODERN STYLE - 481 WORDS

BUTCHER BAKER LIMITED
Re: Escrow Agreement

| Textbook chapters/precedents: | Chapters 24 and 25, Precedent 24.2 |
| | Chapter 4 |

| Dictation names and terms: | Alexander Lenin, Butcher Baker Limited, Michael, Eliad & Redford, Two Hundred Fifty Thousand Dollars ($250,000.00), warranties, instrument, undertaking, Three Hundred Thousand Dollars ($300,000.00), useable, 90 days, genuine, enure,per, president, secretary, Robert B. Redford. |

| Notes: | Backsheet is optional. |

Signing:

                            _____

                            Alexander Lenin

                            BUTCHER BAKER LIMITED

                            Per:

                            _____

                            President

                            _____

                            Secretary

                            MICHAEL, ELIAD & REDFORD

                            Per:

                            _____

                            Robert B. Redford

4.6 LETTER WITH ENCLOSURE - 60 WORDS

Re: Butcher Baker Limited

Inside address:	Mr. John Butcher Butcher Baker Limited Unit 12 345 Republic Road Toronto, Ontario M2W 2H6
Textbook chapters/precedents:	Chapter 5, Precedents 5.1, 5.2, 5.3 Chapter 4
Dictation names and terms:	None.

Notes:

5
REAL ESTATE
LAW

LEGAL TERMINOLOGY

REAL ESTATE LAW

Indicate whether the description of each of the following legal terms is true or false by placing a checkmark in the applicable spaces provided. If necessary, refer to the Glossary in your *Legal Office Procedures* textbook or to a law dictionary:

1. **registry system** - a system for registering land ownership where title is not guaranteed by the government. True ____ False____

2. **land titles system** - a system for registering land ownership where title is guaranteed by the government. True ____ False____

3. **title** - ownership of land. True ____ False____

4. **encroachment** - one person's unauthorized taking of, or adding to his or her own land, an adjoining part of another person's land. True ____ False____

5. **riparian owner** - owner of land which contains a spring or body of water. True ____ False____

6. **life estate** - a life insurance payable during one's lifetime. True ____ False____

7. **joint tenants** - ownership of land by two or more people, with right of survivorship. True ____ False____

8. **tenants in common** - ownership of land where spouses live in common law. True ____ False____

9. **easement** - one owner's right over another owner's land. True ____ False____

10. **right of way** - the right of a landowner to pass over another landowner's land. True ____ False____

Indicate whether the description of each of the following legal terms is true or false by placing a checkmark in the applicable spaces provided. If necessary, refer to the Glossary in your *Legal Office Procedures* textbook or to a law dictionary:

1. **PIN** - property identifier number. True _____ False_____

2. **abstract book** - a book in which the land registry office keeps land ownership records under the registry system. True _____ False_____

3. **parcel register** - a land registry book which summarizes the history of ownership of properties registered under the land titles system. True _____ False_____

4. **possessory title** - the "title" to real property acquired by virtue of continuous, open, and undisturbed possession of such property in the registry system. True _____ False_____

5. **legal description** - description of a person who is over the age of eighteen years. True _____ False_____

6. **right of possession** - a spouse's right of possession (not ownership) of the matrimonial home. True _____ False_____

7. **matrimonial home** - the property which the family uses as its residence. True _____ False_____

8. **transferor** - the party who is selling real property. True _____ False_____

9. **transferee** - the party who is selling real property. True _____ False_____

10. **transfer** - the document that officially transfers title from a seller to a buyer. True _____ False_____

11. **charge** - a debt secured by real property. True _____ False_____

12. **assumed charge** - a charge/mortgage that is existing on the property that the buyer is purchasing which charge/mortgage the buyer is taking over as part of the purchase price. True _____ False_____

13. **charge back** - a charge/mortgage that a person selling a property is taking back from the person buying as part of the purchase price. True _____ False_____

14. **chargor** - a person who owes money on a charge; a borrower. True _____ False_____

15. **chargee** - a person who borrows money. True _____ False_____

Indicate whether the description of each of the following legal terms is true or false by placing a checkmark in the applicable spaces provided. If necessary, refer to the Glossary in your *Legal Office Procedures* textbook or to a law dictionary:

1. **statement of adjustments** - a document listing the amounts of money credited to each of the purchaser and the vendor to be applied toward the purchase price. True ____ False____

2. **direction regarding funds** - a document by which a client authorizes a party to pay money to the client's law firm instead of directly to the client. True ____ False____

3. **discharge statement** - a document that sets out the balance of principal and interest owing on a charge/mortgage for purposes of paying off the charge/mortgage. True ____ False____

4. **statutory declaration** - a document parallel to an affidavit by which a party declares the facts in it are true. True ____ False____

5. **undertaking** - a written promise to do something. True ____ False____

6. **closing date** - the date on which the land registry office is closed. True ____ False____

7. **execution search** - a search for any writs of seizure and sale filed with the sheriff. True ____ False____

8. **direction regarding title** - a document that directs how a purchaser wishes to own the real property. True ____ False____

9. **letter of requisitions** - a letter by a purchaser's solicitor requiring certain things be done in order to clear up problems on title. True ____ False____

10. **land transfer tax** - tax a purchaser pays when purchasing personal property. True ____ False____

11. **land transfer tax statements/affidavit** - a document that sets out the purchase price of the property for purposes of calculating and paying land transfer tax. True ____ False____

12. **property taxes** - taxes paid on real property by a municipality. True ____ False ____

13. **discharge of charge** - a document that is registered when a charge/mortgage is prepared. True ____ False____

14. **power of sale** - a clause in a charge/mortgage which empowers the chargee/mortgagee, upon the chargor's/mortgagor's default in payment, to sell the property to satisfy the debt. True ____ False____

15. **foreclosure** - a litigation action by which a chargee or mortgagee becomes the legal owner of real property after the chargor or mortgagor has defaulted in payment. True ____ False____

16. **judicial sale** - a sale by a sheriff as a result of an unpaid judgment. True ___ False___

17. **condominium** - a system of land ownership of individual units that are within a multi-unit structure. True ___ False___

18. **common elements** - those parts of the condominium that are owned in common with all the unit owners. True ___ False___

19. **condominium corporation status certificate** - a certificate which a condominium corporation gives to a purchaser, showing whether the owner of the unit being purchased has paid all common elements expenses. True ___ False___

20. **title search** - a search of the history of ownership of a particular property to ensure clear title to the purchaser. True ___ False___

GRAMMAR BRUSH-UP

A. RUN-ON SENTENCES AND COMMA SPLICES - REFRESHER

Indicate which of the following sentences is a run-on (RO), which is a comma splice (CSp), and which is a complete/correct sentence (CS). See Chapter 4 in your *Legal Office Procedures* textbook for help on run-on sentences and comma splices.

> **Legal TIP**
>
> A run-on sentence is one that places no punctuation between two complete sentences. A comma splice is one that places a comma between two complete sentences (including sentences that contain transitional phrases such as nevertheless, for example, in fact, on the other hand, however, therefore, furthermore).

1. Jack studied philosophy Jill studied science. RO ___ CSp ___ CS ___

2. Jack studied philosophy, Jill studied science. RO ___ CSp ___ CS ___

3. Jack disliked philosophy, however he studied very hard.
   RO ___ CSp ___ CS ___

4. The college will close at noon today it will remain closed for the next three days.
   RO ___ CSp ___ CS ___

5. The college will close at noon today and will remain closed for the next three days.
   RO ___ CSp ___ CS ___

6. The college will close at noon today, it will remain closed for the next three days.
   RO ___ CSp ___ CS ___

7. The witness came forward, his testimony was damaging to our client.
   RO ___ CSp ___ CS ___

8. The witness came forward, however his testimony was damaging to our client.
   RO ___ CSp ___ CS ___

9. The witness came forward; however, his testimony was damaging to our client.
   RO ___ CSp ___ CS ___

10. The witness came forward but his testimony was damaging to our client.
    RO ___ CSp ___ CS ___

Use a comma, a semicolon, a period and/or an applicable coordinating conjunction to correct or make the following sentences complete. Use CS to indicate any sentences that are complete sentences. See Chapter 4 in your *Legal Office Procedures* textbook for examples on how to fix run-on sentences and comma splices.

1. Jack studied philosophy Jill studied science.

2. Jack studied philosophy, Jill studied science.

3. Jack disliked philosophy, however he studied very hard.

4. The college will close at noon today it will remain closed for the next three days.

5. The college will close at noon today and will remain closed for the next three days.

6. The college will close at noon today, it will remain closed for the next three days.

7. The witness came forward, his testimony was damaging to our client.

8. The witness came forward, however his testimony was damaging to our client.

9. The witness came forward; however, his testimony was damaging to our client.

10. The witness came forward but his testimony was damaging to our client.

Textbook chapters/precedents: Chapters 4 and 6

Dictation names and terms: <u>Canadian Law</u>, rules of club, properly constituted.

Notes:

FORMAT

Key the opening paragraph of Justice Zuber's dictation flush with the left margin, and set off (block indent) all remaining paragraphs to indicate a long quotation. Begin new paragraphs (all set off) at the following points of dictation, in order of occurrence:

Much of our conduct...

The state representing...

Legal TIP

Remember to set off long quotations but do not enclose them in quotation marks. Setting off replaces the need for quotation marks. If there are quotations within the set-off quotation, use double quotation marks.

5.2 LETTER REPLYING TO REQUISITIONS - 295 WORDS

Re: Solomon sale to King
         100 Sisyphus Road, Toronto

Inside address:	Castles & Sands Barristers and Solicitors Suite 900 205 Portage Street Markham, Ontario L3R 3G3 Attention: Mr. Raymond G. Castles
Textbook chapters/precedents:	Chapters 5 and 35 Chapter 5, Precedents 5.1, 5.2, 5.3 Chapter 4
Dictation names and terms:	chattels, fair wear and tear, undertaking, encumbrances, requisitions, survey, construction liens, executions.

Notes:

5.3 REPORTING LETTER, SALE - 327 WORDS

Re: Your sale to King, 100 Sisyphus Road, Toronto

Inside address:	Mr. and Mrs. David Solomon 96 Atlantic Avenue Toronto, Ontario M2V 2H6
Textbook chapters/precedents:	Chapters 5 and 35, Precedent 35.11 Chapter 4

Dictation names and terms: transfer/deed, Sydney Haden King, Renee Pamela King, foregoing, Susanna, direction regarding title.

Notes:

NEW FILE 📁

CAIN, Nicholas and Stephanie
Re: Purchase of 2 Brothers Road, Toronto

In this file, we act for Nicholas and Stephanie Cain who are purchasing the above property. The transcription in this file enables you to see how a purchase and sale transaction might gradually unfold in the legal office.

WORD Processing

The following information is frequently used in this file. Using the applicable word processing features, create a template and save it for each subsequent use in this file:

Re: Cain purchase from Abel
        2 Brothers Road, Toronto

Inside address: Mr. Raymond G. Castles
Castles & Sands
Barristers and Solicitors
Suite 900
205 Portage Street
Markham, Ontario
L3R 3G3

5.4 LETTER REGARDING TITLE - 126 WORDS

Re: Cain purchase from Abel
        2 Brothers Road, Toronto

Inside address:	Castles & Sands Barristers and Solicitors Suite 900 205 Portage Street Markham, Ontario L3R 3G3 Attention: Mr. Raymond G. Castles
Textbook chapters/precedents:	Chapters 5 and 36, Precedent 36.2 Chapter 4
Dictation names and terms:	vendors, Nicholas Windsor, Stephanie Denise, June 16 (35 yrs. ago), July 13, (33 yrs. ago), as joint tenants.

Notes:

5.5 LETTER OF REQUISITIONS - 636 WORDS

Re: Cain purchase from Abel
        2 Brothers Road, Toronto

Inside address:	Mr. Raymond G. Castles Castles & Sands Barristers and Solicitors Suite 900 205 Portage Street Markham, Ontario L3R 3G3
Textbook chapters/precedents:	Chapters 5 and 36, Precedent 36.15 Chapter 4

| Dictation names and terms: | without prejudice, requisitions, survey, discharge, liens, charges/mortgage, and/or encumbrances, easements, rights-of-way, rights-of-encumbrance, chattels, Land Registry Office, urea formaldehyde foam, work orders, deficiency notices, by-law, non-resident, Income Tax Act of Canada, contravened, Planning Act, Family Law Act, Instrument No. 123456, Christian Vidaal, Christine Vidaal, $150,000.00, July 8, (five years ago), institutional, undertaking, declaration of possession, warranties. |

Notes:

5.6 REPORTING LETTER TO CHARGEE/MORTGAGEE - 315 WORDS

Re: Cain purchase from Abel
       2 Brothers Road, Toronto
       First Charge/Mortgage, Loan No. 808181

Inside address:	Dyss Trust Company
	55 Rodeo Drive
	Toronto, Ontario
	M2K 1T1
	Attention: Ms. Alexandra Kirkev, Lending Officer
Textbook chapters/precedents:	Chapters 5 and 36, Precedent 36.23
	Chapter 4
Dictation names and terms:	March 17, (this yr.), registered duplicate charge/mortgage, Instrument No. TB423649, encroachment, ideal, vendors, sworn, declaration of possession.

Notes:

Re: Your purchase from Abel, 2 Brothers Road, Toronto

Inside address:	Mr. and Mrs. Nicholas Cain 2 Brothers Road Toronto, Ontario M2W 6L6
Textbook chapters/precedents:	Chapters 5 and 36, Precedent 36.23 Chapter 4
Dictation names and terms:	transfer/deed, Instrument No. TB343434, Nicholas Windsor Cain, Stephanie Denise Cain, good and marketable title, encumbrance, restrictions, Construction Lien Act, abutting, breach, executions, statement of adjustments, $205,198.19, 10,000.00, Treasurer, there are arrears, solicitor's undertaking, $198.19, oil burner, Personal Property Security Act, chattels, land transfer tax, $1,875.00, charge/mortgage, Dyss Trust Company, $182,750.00, 6.7 percent, $1,375.00, Oscar Chip, O.L.S., June 3, 1927, adverse possession, encroachments, Family Law Act, Land Transfer Tax Act, warranty, Urea Formaldehyde Foam Insulation (UFFI), UFFI, standard charge terms, amortization schedule, declaration of possession, bill of sale and warranties, execution certificate.

Notes:

6
ESTATES LAW

LEGAL TERMINOLOGY

ESTATES

Indicate whether the description of each of the following legal terms is true or false by placing a checkmark in the applicable spaces provided. If necessary, refer to the Glossary in your *Legal Office Procedures* textbook or to a law dictionary:

1. **will**- a document outlining how a person wishes his or her property to be dealt with after his or her death. True _____ False_____

2. **codicil** - a document by which a person may make changes to his or her executed will. True _____ False_____

3. **beneficiary** - a person to whom something is given in a will. True _____ False_____

4. **estate** - all property a deceased owns at death. True _____ False_____

5. **inter vivos** - usually referring to a gift made while the parties are living. True _____ False_____

6. **domicile** - place of a person's permanent residence. True _____ False_____

7. **testator** - a male person who gives testimony at trial. True _____ False_____

8. **testatrix** - a female person who makes a will. True _____ False_____

9. **testate** - a female person who dies having made a will. True _____ False_____

10. **equalization payment** - the net family property of spouses, divided in half. True _____ False_____

Indicate whether the description of each of the following legal terms is true or false by placing a checkmark in the applicable spaces provided. If necessary, refer to the Glossary in your *Legal Office Procedures* textbook or to a law dictionary:

1. **preferential share** - the equalization payment to which a surviving spouse is by law given preference of entitlement. True ____ False____

2. **per capita** - equal division of an estate among beneficiaries on the basis of head count. True ____ False____

3. **issue** - children or descendants. True ____ False____

4. **net family property** - the net value of property that married spouses accumulate during marriage. True ____ False____

5. **per stirpes** - division of an estate on the basis of representation of the same lineal stock or the same family. The beneficiary takes the share to which his or her deceased ancestor would have been entitled. True ____ False____

6. **surety** - a person who has signed a bond. True ____ False____

7. **notarial certificate** - a certificate which a notary public signs and attaches to a copy of a document to certify that the copy is not identical to the original. True ____ False____

8. **survivorship application** - a document which a surviving joint tenant registers in the land titles system to transfer the deceased's share of the property over to his or her own name alone. True ____ False____

9. **transmission application** - a document filed in the land titles office to have title transferred to the name of the personal representative of a deceased owner to enable the personal representative to deal with the property. True ____ False____

10. **passing of accounts** - an examination by the court of an estate's assets, payments, and debts in order to approve the completion of the estate. True ____ False____

GRAMMAR BRUSH-UP

A. POSSESSIVES - REFRESHER

This exercise contains selections from the transcription. Place an apostrophe (') in the place/s where one is required. Place an x over/next to any incorrectly applied apostrophes. If the wording contains a correctly applied apostrophe, indicate so by writing correct (C) at the end of the wording which contains the correctly applied apostrophe. See Chapter 4 in your *Legal Office Procedures* textbook for the rules on the use of the apostrophe and possessives.

1. The sheriffs office; its' not far from here.

2. A Trustees absolute and uncontrolled discretion.

3. Such beneficiarys income.

4. Mr. Domris common law spouse.

5. The deceaseds legal spouse.

6. Its a claimants statement.

7. A physicians statement.

8. The coroners report.

9. The funeral directors statement.

10. Our firms trust cheque.

NEW FILE 🗁

DOMRI, Eric
Re: Estate

In this file, we act for Mrs. Jenny Domri in making an application to collect death benefits from various insurance policies that her husband, Eric Domri, had taken out. Eric Domri was killed when he accidentally fell down an elevator shaft at his place of employment.

The transcription in this file sequentially carries this file to completion and to preparing Jenny Domri's will. This type of file continuity adds meaning to your transcription as it enables you to see how estate files might gradually unfold in the legal office.

W≡ WORD Processing

The following information is frequently used in this file. Using the applicable word processing features, create a template and save it for each subsequent use in this file:

Inside address: Mrs. Jenny Domri
                                   345 Patton Street
                                   Toronto, Ontario
                                   M4N 6A3

6.1 MEMO TO FILE - 257 WORDS

Re: Domri Estate

Textbook chapters/precedents: Chapters 6, Precedent 6.2
                                   Chapters 4, 5, 6, 39, and 41

Dictation names and terms: File, Domri Estate, Eric Domri, Lift International, death benefits, Andrea Caplan, benefits coordinator, optional life insurance, Kingston Life Insurance Company, accidental death benefits, Windsor Insurance Company, Lucinda Russo, Brazil, enrolment form.

Notes:

6.2 LETTER - 201 WORDS

Re: Estate of Eric Domri

Inside address:	Ms. Andrea Caplan Lift International 8090 Blair Street Toronto, Ontario M3B 2U2
Textbook chapters/precedents:	Chapter 5, Precedents 5.1, 5.2, 5.3 Chapter 4
Dictation names and terms:	Jenny Domri, $30,000.00, Ms. Lucinda Russo, Brazil, Kingston Life Insurance, Windsor Insurance Company.

Notes:

6.3 LETTER WITH SECOND PAGE HEADING - 423 WORDS

Re: Estate of Eric Domri

Inside address:	Mrs. Jenny Domri 345 Patton Street Toronto, Ontario M4N 6A3
Textbook chapters/precedents:	Chapter 5, Second and subsequent page headings Chapter 5, Precedents 5.1, 5.2, 5.3 Chapter 4

| Dictation names and terms: | Lift International, $15,000.00, $3,000.00, Lucinda Russo, Brazil, enrolment form, Kingston Life Insurance Company, certificate of appointment of estate trustee without a will (letters of administration), discharge, proof of death, Windsor Insurance Company, in lieu. |

Notes:

6.4 LETTER WITH ENCLOSURE - 268 WORDS

Re: Estate of Eric Domri

| Inside address: | Ms. Andrea Caplan
Lift International
8090 Blair Street
Toronto, Ontario
M3B 2U2 |

| Textbook chapters/precedents: | Chapter 5, Second and subsequent page headings
Chapter 5, Precedents 5.1, 5.2, 5.3
Chapter 4 |

| Dictation names and terms: | Jenny Domri, 1. Certificate of appointment of estate trustee without a will (letters of administration), Windsor Insurance Company, notarized, statement of death, Kingston Life Insurance Company, Kingston Life election method. |

Notes:

6.5 LETTER WITH ENCLOSURE - 134 WORDS

Re: Estate of Eric Domri

Inside address:	Mr. Richard Callow Callow & Callous Barristers and Solicitors 49 Young-Hard Road Toronto, Ontario M6P 7R4
Textbook chapters/precedents:	Chapter 5, Precedents 5.1, 5.2, 5.3 Chapter 4
Dictation names and terms:	$10,000.00, Lucinda Russo.

Notes:

6.6 LETTER WITH ENCLOSURE - 205 WORDS

Re: Estate of Eric Domri

Inside address:	Mrs. Jenny Domri 345 Patton Street Toronto, Ontario M4N 6A3
Textbook chapters/precedents:	Chapter 5, Precedents 5.1, 5.2, 5.3 Chapter 4
Dictation names and terms:	order on consent, payment out of court, accrued, $60,230.00, Callow & Callous, Lucinda Russo, $10,000.00, $46,359.81.

Notes:

6.7 WILL - 1,978 WORDS

DOMRI, Jenny
Re: Will

Textbook chapters/precedents:	Chapter 39, Precedent 39.1 Chapter 4
Dictation names and terms:	Jenny Domri, Toronto, Ontario, testament, nominate, constitute, Matilda Hades, executrix and trustee, my "Trustee," thirty days, Steven Rupert Domri, Lawrence Justin Domri, beneficiaries, successors annuitant, devise and bequeath, succession duties, codicil, commute, residue, George Henry Gillilland, uncontrolled discretion, age of twenty-five, community of property, Family Law Act, prognosis, prolonged coma, heroic, preceding (blank)* pages, subscribed, testatrix.

Notes:	Prepare a will cover. *In the blank, key the total number of previous pages of the will.

Ending of will:

SIGNED, PUBLISHED AND DECLARED) by the said JENNY DOMRI,) as and for her last Will and) Testament, in the presence of us,) both present at the same time, who) at her request, in her presence, and) in the presence of each other, have) subscribed our names as witnesses.)	

_____
Jenny Domri

Signature of witness _____
Print name _____
Address _____
Occupation _____

Signature of witness _____
Print name _____
Address _____
Occupation _____

<u>Re: Will</u>

Inside address:	Mrs. Jenny Domri 345 Patton Street Toronto, Ontario M4N 6A3
Textbook chapters/precedents:	Chapter 5, Precedents 5.1, 5.2, 5.3 Chapter 4
Dictation names and terms:	Matilda Hades, estate trustee with a will (executrix).

Notes:

Re: Decision on Murder Case

TRANSCRIBED VERSION OF ITEM 6.9

Following is the transcribed version of Item 6.9. Unless otherwise instructed,

(a)   out of class, listen through the dictation while following the transcribed version below just to enjoy Justice Scollin's reasons for judgment on a murder case that came before him, and/or

(b)   transcribe this Item 6.9 while simultaneously following the transcribed version of it which follows below. If so, follow the same format as that shown below.

I give you some extracts from a case in which the accused was eventually convicted by the jury of manslaughter, and that verdict was supported on appeal. What I am quoting from is a ruling given during the trial about whether certain evidence was admissible, and you'll see that this impinges on the third area that I am going to talk about, the <u>Charter of Rights</u>. This is a case called (the Queen against James Skinner) <u>R. v. James Skinner</u>. These are the portions that set the stage for the decision:

> Stripped of juristic trappings, the issue is whether the law hides the truth from the jury. The truth is that evidence of what the accused said to undercover police officers, at a time when he was a prime suspect but not in detention, would assist the jury in deciding whether the accused committed murder. Indeed, without this evidence, the Crown could not make its case against the accused.

> The victim, a boy from Stonewall, Manitoba, died in early December 1979, but his body remained hidden in the snow until the middle of April 1980. As a result of the investigation that followed, which included many interviews by members of six teams of the Royal Canadian Mounted Police, the accused, a Stonewall resident, was a prime suspect. Acting on his lawyer's advice, he refused to be interviewed, but later, through his lawyer, he supplied work time sheets in support of a questionable alibi.

> Electronic surveillance authorized in May 1980 proved fruitless as the accused moved away from the province. Having eliminated all other suspects, but having insufficient evidence to charge and arrest the accused, the police left the case open but dormant until 1990. On reviewing it at that time, they decided that the only remaining investigative method of solving the crime was the resorting to an undercover operation in combination with renewed electronic surveillance.

In November 1990, they took the opportunity for the principal undercover officer, Constable Jean Gagnon, in the guise of an escorted prisoner, to become acquainted with the accused whom they were escorting from his home in Vancouver to face charges laid by the City of Winnipeg police.

Later, in May 1991, having traced the accused to his new address in Vancouver, they obtained an authorization from Madam Justice Ryan of the Supreme Court of British Columbia to intercept the accused's private communications. Later in May 1991, when Constable Gagnon "befriended" the accused in Vancouver, incriminating statements by the accused were recorded which provided the police with the evidence to arrest him.

The accused objects to the jury hearing this evidence on the grounds that the authorization was invalid and that the police violated his right to silence. The issue, then, is whether the <u>Charter</u> or the common law requires the court to suppress this evidence from the jury.

(Having decided that various legal objections were unfounded, I went on to consider the essential claim that his right to silence was breached.)

****

Note: The rest of Justice Scollin's reasons for judgment continues in the draft set out below. To learn what happened in this murder case, key the judgment in wording and format exactly as set out below, except check it for Gertrude's spelling; there are three spelling errors.

(In the result, I concluded my reasoning as follows:)

Leaving open the possible effect of actual coercive or oppressive conduct or interrogation by the police, neither the <u>Charter of Rights</u> nor the common law supports the exclusion of the evidence in this case, and in this regard, I need refer only briefly to the nature of the stratagem employed in the undercover operation.

The undercover operator took oblique steps to lead the suspect round to discussing the case by appearing to unburden his conscience with a touching story from his fictional past in which he caused the death of a younger brother by disconnecting life-support systems in a Montreal hospital. By his account, this younger brother had been reduced to a permanent coma as a result of a traffic accident when the undercover officer was driving under the influence of drugs. This story also served as an excuse for the officer's claimed resolve never again to smoke marijuana and, therefore, to refuse the regular joints offered by the accused.

In addition, as the acused appeared to be obsessed by the polygraph and how it could be "beaten," the undercover introduced this topic, thereby leading the accused to discuss the death of the boy. As the "friendship" developed, the officer asked questions in a natural and comradely fashion, which resulted in the accused talking about his part in the Stonewall incident.

There can be no doubt that the "unburdening of conscience" scenario was the major cause of the accused making the admission that he did, which he explained, after his arrest, as being a concocted story designed to relieve the anxiety of his friend, the undercover officer. The concept of a "functional equivalent" of an interrogation is difficult to define and to apply in the abstract, but in the circumstances disclosed by the recorded conversations, I am not satisfied that even if the <u>Boyles</u> case applied, the accused was subjected in this case to any interrogation, other than that which was appropriate to the scenario.

The diffrence between the unpalatable and the inedible is generally a matter of personal taste. Absent "dirty tricks," the courts should not set themselves up as the arbiters of good taste or of the preferred methods of investigation. It is unrealistic to demand chivalry from those who must investigate what are often heinous offences against blameless victims. The law should not materialize as a revolutionary rabbit from a judicial magician's hat.

Both the common law and the <u>Charter</u> justly preserve the accused from coercion and endow him with specific rights which he may exercice at the time of his arrest and while he is in custody; but the courts should not be so indulgent as to preserve the accused from himself and his own untrammelled tongue, and should require realistic justification for suppressing facts from the jury which go to weight rather than to admissibility. Juries often hear such an expurgated version of reality that they tend to become triers of fiction rather than masters of fact.

Finally, in my view, the courts must not lend moral legitimacy or credence to the fanciful perception that law enforcement is a hostile invasion of individual rights rather than a defensive affirmation by society of individual duties. Individual rights deserve respect but not veneration; and if, on returning from each pilgrimage to the <u>Charter</u>, the courts claim yet another miracle of enlightenment, a skeptical society may eventually be justified in classing the miracles as mirages and the recording of them as philosophism.

Accordingly, I have concluded that the jury is entitled to hear the truth, that is, that the accused made relevant statements which must, in the interest of justice, be heard and weighed.

****

Re: Charter of Rights

TRANSCRIBED VERSION OF ITEM 6.10

Following is the transcribed version of Item 6.10. Unless otherwise instructed,

(a)   out of class, listen through the dictation while following the transcribed version below just to enjoy Justice Scollin's surprising thoughts on the Canadian Charter of Rights, and/or

(b)   transcribe this Item 6.10 while simultaneously following the transcribed version of it which follows below. If so, follow the same format as that shown below.

Finally, with growing confidence that this machine and I eventually may resolve our little problems and get together, I move on to the last of the areas that I want to say a few words about. That is, this--as I have called it--much vaunted <u>Charter of Rights</u> which came into force in Canada in April of 1982. It is a significant document which changes the whole balance of state power that previously existed.

Following the British tradition which still applies in Britain, Parliament, the elected representatives of the people, is still supreme. There, in Britain, no <u>Charter</u> or trammel exists on the power of Parliament, but in some ways copying the American system, Canada, in 1982, as part of the patriation process of the Constitution, adopted a <u>Charter of Rights</u>. In the result, Parliament in most areas is no longer supreme. In the worst scenario, Canada is now governed by the majority, which may be five to four of the Supreme Court of Canada--nine lawyers, selected by Ottawa on a representative basis who are non-elected but who have enormous power.

The Supreme Court of Canada is the final arbiter of what our Constitution means. It may decide that any act of a province or of Ottawa contravenes the <u>Charter</u>. That decision by the nine un-elected, or at worst by the one that swings the vote, is how the validity of laws is now determined. Before 1982, Canada was in the same position as exists still in the United Kingdom. Parliament is supreme.

Now, the situation is radically different. Under the <u>Charter</u>, the Supreme Court of Canada has the final word on the meaning of the Constitution, and section 52 of the Constitution Act says that laws that contravene or are not in accordance with the dictates of the Constitution are of no force or effect. In the result, the Supreme Court is in fact the ultimate arbiter of morals, legality, and utility of much of the legislation passed by either provinces or the federal government.

While it is indeed a valuable and humane document, coming as I do from a different background, I am always suspicious of having judges, that is, people such as myself, determine the absolute values of any society, and accordingly, I sometimes say reasonably naughty things about the <u>Charter</u> as it has been used and interpreted, such as "the <u>Charter</u> is a bag of goodies for the baddies," and given some of the bizarre arguments on trivial cases that I see, "the <u>Charter</u> has proved to be a fertile father of a host of illegitimate, intellectual offspring."

Students of Ms. Kamakaris, that is the end. Thank you for listening.

****

TRANSCRIPTION INFORMATION *FOR* TEST BANK

1. LETTER - 203 WORDS

Inside address:

Mr. and Mrs. Frederick Templeton
49 Second Avenue
Toronto, Ontario
M8U 2J6

2. LETTER - 216 WORDS

Inside address:

Mr. Roger Best
Best and Bungle
Barristers and Solicitors
39 Park Avenue
Toronto, Ontario
M6E 1A2

3. LETTER - 271 WORDS

Inside address:

Ms. Catherine Nestrum
910 Grove Street
Toronto, Ontario
M8J 1P2

4. LETTER - 293 WORDS

Inside address:

Mrs. Jenny Domri
345 Patton Street
Toronto, Ontario
M4N 6A3

5. LETTER - 296 WORDS

Inside address:

Flanders Field
Barristers and Solicitors
3 John McCrae Road
Toronto, Ontario
M4V 2U6

Attention: Mr. Ingmar Flanders

6. LETTER - 320 WORDS

Inside address: Mr. Jason Argonaut
                                         96 Golden Fleece Road
                                         Sydney, Nova Scotia
                                         B1H 6J4

7. LETTER BY COURIER, WITH ENCLOSURE - 194 WORDS

Inside address: Mr. Trevor Gorgon
                                         Castalia Springs Incorporated
                                         800 Delphi Road
                                         Toronto, Ontario
                                         M1V 6J6

Special notation/s: BY COURIER

8. LETTER WITHOUT PREJUDICE - 300 WORDS

Inside address: Safe-T-First Incorporated
                                         14 Little Treasures Road
                                         Vancouver, BC
                                         V2M 4D8

Special notation/s: WITHOUT PREJUDICE

9. MEMORANDUM - 221 WORDS

TO: David Eliad

10. MEMO OF LAW - CORPORATE AND COMMERCIAL LAW - 270 WORDS

Re: Mega Software Incorporated v. John Shiek

Memo to: David W. Eliad

                                         Re Nandrajog 1981

11. MEMO OF LAW - REAL ESTATE - 322 WORDS

Re: Hamilton Transaction

Memo to: David W. Eliad

                                        Wilson Pitts
                                        McVity v. Tranouth (1905), (1908).

12. MEMO OF LAW - FAMILY LAW - 377 WORDS

Re: Weigh v. Chan

Memo to: David W. Eliad
                                        Ken Weigh
                                        Fulcher v. Near (1982)
                                        Thornborrow v. MacKinnon (1981)